MAN IN SEARCH OF HIS ANCESTORS

Part of a painting
in Cueva del Civil,
Castellón, Spain

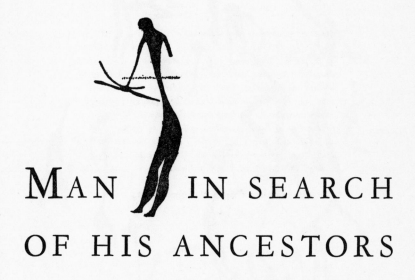

MAN IN SEARCH
OF HIS ANCESTORS

The Romance of Paleontology by ANDRÉ SENET

Translated by MALCOLM BARNES

McGRAW-HILL BOOK COMPANY, INC.

New York   Toronto   London

CONTENTS

PLATES

CHARTS AND TABLES

ILLUSTRATIONS IN TEXT

MAN IN SEARCH OF HIS ANCESTORS

The Monkey's Revenge

SATURDAY, November 21st, 1953, was for the great majority of Londoners a Saturday of no importance: the weather was gloomy, the sky was low, the red omnibuses crowded the centre of the city, signs glittered in Piccadilly Circus, and starlings twittered in Trafalgar Square. Nothing had changed.

Nevertheless, it was no ordinary Saturday. Aloof from all this activity, down in the west, not far from the quiet spaces of Kensington Gardens, a number of laboratory assistants were busy under the direction of a departmental head. The next day, being a Sunday, there would be many visitors to the Natural History Museum at South Kensington, the children more numerous than the adults. Now, on the morning of November 21st there had appeared the usual monthly bulletin of the geological department of the Natural History Museum, and in a few lines this contained a sensational communication that had left the majority of its readers flabbergasted and had raised a cry of triumph from a few others. For forty years the scientists had been hoaxed and the Piltdown man was really nothing but a fake. Its jaw, which had been regarded as a true antiquity, was no more and no less than the jaw-bone of an ape—an orang-utan or a chimpanzee—that had probably been alive at the beginning of the century in the reign of the good King Edward VII.

That is why, in the ground-floor galleries of the museum, on the left, some twenty yards from the entrance, they were in a hurry to change the glass case where the casts of the Piltdown man were displayed. These specimens, hitherto regarded as being about 40,000 years old, had been under investigation by one of the world's most celebrated anatomists, Professor W. le Gros Clark. For the second time in four years, the lower jaw, the solitary canine and the fragments of the cranium had been subjected to the merciless test of microchemical examination. They did not emerge with credit. On the first occasion, in 1949, it had been necessary to rate the Piltdown fossil considerably younger than was thought. It was not from 75 to 100,000 years old, but 40,000 at the very most. On the second occasion it was necessary to rate it even lower: at least a part of the fossil had been faked. And there was reason for the excitement, for the bomb had been thrown by three world-famous scientists. It was Dr. Weiner of the Department of Anatomy at the University of Oxford who "belled the cat" and energetically demanded a re-examination of the bones, and it was his chief, the famous Professor le Gros Clark, and Dr. Oakley, a well-known prehistorian on the staff of the Natural History Museum, who had closely collaborated in this revaluation.

But who was this venerable person, this pillar of the museum, casts and photos of whose bones had been sent around the world so that they might be submitted to the pitiless criticism of the experts? This Piltdown man is more than a humble nameless fossil. He is a veritable symbol. By the studies, discussions and even the disputes he has provoked, he shows us, probably better than any other fossil, the exciting hunt which man has carried on in search of his ancestors; moreover, he shamelessly reveals both the strength and weakness of paleontology, and of all the natural sciences in a more general way.

So on this notable Saturday of November 21st, 1953, the prehistorians took their revenge on the Piltdown man. The brief article which brought about his fall would scarcely have attracted attention if the newspapers in Britain, Europe and America had not devoted to him some lengthy articles that were decorated with a few quite misleading caricatures. For forty-eight hours radio and television sought out the prehistorians in order to drag them before the microphone. Queen Elizabeth might be leaving for her 174-day tour of the world, the French National Assembly might be carrying on a noisy debate about the European Army, and the police investigations into the triple murder at Lurs might be in full swing; but all these events had to share the front page of the newspapers with headlines that announced the exposure of the greatest scientific fraud of the half-century. A few old bits of bone and a few worn teeth were enough to stampede the journalists. Articles and interviews about these rusty remains, hitherto known only to experts, were hastily concocted.

Yet the excitement was surprising. One would like to be sure

that the journalists and radio-reporters were not obeying some
unconscious impulse; and after careful reflection I think that the
layman has seen in this affair an opportunity to take his revenge
on the scientists. Nuclear physics threatens us with its explosions,
and paleontology has had to pay for the damage done by splitting
the atom. Moreover, there is the curious fact that on the very day
the Piltdown fraud was exposed, one of the most eminent atomic
scientists in America, Dr. Robert Oppenheimer, reported the discovery of new nuclear particles and stated that our knowledge of
this realm of physics might be greatly upset thereby.

And all this because a very clever forger—it is still impossible to
say exactly who he was, but it was possibly Mr. Dawson himself—
had, by the skilful use of a file and a small bottle of potassium
bichromate, disguised the bone of an ape as a human fossil. It is
worth giving some attention to the matter, for in the end it raises
the problem of the origin of man and, by inference, of the origins
of life on the earth, forcing one at the same time to question the
confidence that can be placed in the prehistoric discoveries which
are used for their interpretation.

According to the story that had so far been accepted, it all began
in a quite commonplace fashion one summer day in 1908. A little
man of 44 years, with curling moustaches and bowler hat, was
walking quietly along a quiet road in the County of Sussex, in
the neighbourhood of Uckfield. He had almost arrived at the
village of Fletching and had just passed quite close to a farm
belonging to the hamlet of Piltdown. He suddenly stopped,
stepped back a few paces and reflected. He had just noticed that
certain parts of the road had been repaired with small flat, reddish
gravel which he did not know existed in that locality. Now Mr.
Charles Dawson, a solicitor of Newhaven, was also a keen
amateur in "things of the past." He was interested in archaeology
and geology, and he had a very definite weakness for paleontology. Always on the lookout for a discovery, he soon questioned
the workmen and learned that the gravel came from a small quarry
nearby; he asked if anyone had found any bones there and
obtained a promise that if any should turn up he would be advised
at once.

Soon the foreman in charge of the work on the farm (so the
story goes) gave him a small fragment of a flat bone that was
reddish like the gravel, so like the gravel in fact that one could well

believe that the greater part of the Piltdown skull was lost simply
because the rust had been so abundantly deposited as to make it
practically impossible for a layman to distinguish between bone
and gravel. It seemed, moreover, that the workmen had on one
occasion broken "a sort of large coconut," as one of them said,
without having paid the least attention to it. The forger who had
made the jaw-bone had known how to produce this reddish
coloration with diabolical skill.

The bone which the foreman had just given Mr. Dawson was
part of the cranium; it was a fragment of the left parietal, that is to
say, a fragment of one of those two roughly rectangular bones
which form the top of the head, stretching side by side
between the forehead and the nape and fitting together with little
pointed teeth in such a way as to trace a sinuous line—the
parietal join—that separates the brain-pan into left and right
halves.

After this first discovery, irresistibly drawn by the Piltdown
gravel pits, Charles Dawson returned to them again and again.
But for three years his tenacity went unrewarded. There was
nothing to be found in the gravel. In 1911 he himself started to
poke about in a small pile of gravel dumped beside the pit. He
extracted from it another fragment of parietal bone. Here is a
point which it is important to stress straight away: the two fragments of parietal bone were never found properly embedded in a
particular geological layer; they were found among the material
that had been excavated and this was the case with all the remains
of the Piltdown man discovered thereafter. This was one of the
principal arguments used by its adversaries in discussion concerning the fossil.

However, after this further discovery, Charles Dawson hesitated no longer. He contacted an expert at London's Natural
History Museum, Professor Arthur Smith Woodward, the paleontologist. The two of them engaged some workmen, obtained
the necessary permission, and in the spring of 1912 began to
search the little quarry carefully. They extracted several scraps of
skull and the right half of a jaw-bone. Woodward at once undertook the complete reconstruction of the skull on the basis of the
few fragments he possessed and found that the volume of the
brain, at 1,070 c.c., was a little less than that of modern man.
Here, therefore, was man's ideal ancestor: man at the dawn of

humanity. For this reason Woodward named him *Eoanthropus Dawsoni*.

The volume of the brain is known to experts as "cranial capacity" and is expressed in cubic centimetres. Generally, it is between 1,400 and 1,600 c.c. in men and between 1,300 and 1,450 c.c. in women. While stating the volume of the brain it gives at the same time some indication of the degree of intelligence, although many other facts also come into play. Nevertheless, if this cranial capacity makes a comparison between the ancestors of man, the men of to-day, and the larger apes possible, it cannot be used in comparisons between man and other animals since the size of the animal is then involved, a factor which may falsify the results.

However that may be, on December 18th, 1912, Smith Woodward and Charles Dawson made a resounding communication to the Geological Society of London and showed its members the various bones that had been extracted from the quarry. Feelings ran high in scientific circles and amongst the public. The more important newspapers seized upon the discovery, just as 40 years later they were to seize upon the fall of the Piltdown man. For in 1912 the matter was important to Englishmen. This was the first time a fossil ancestor of modern man had been discovered in England, while France, Germany and Belgium already had several such fossils. And this fossil, this ancient citizen of the British Isles, provided (or so most people thought) a very fine missing-link between apes and man, but with an ape's jaw he had just upset all the accepted ideas of 50 years concerning human evolution. The affair became a sensation. Tourists flocked to Piltdown and the local inn—which had changed its commonplace sign of *The Lamb* for one with much greater publicity value, *The Piltdown Man*—did a lot of trade.

But the great quarrel of the Piltdown man had only just begun. The French, proud of having seen the birth of the science of prehistory on their own soil, and the Americans, who, in default of possessing any venerable prehuman remains at home, were already taking an interest in Western Europe, at once took up a position opposed to the English. For them the matter was not in doubt: bones of two different individuals (by the greatest chance, certainly!) happened to be found so close together that they were mistaken for parts of the skeleton of one individual. Unfortunately the same coincidence was to be repeated in 1915, when Dawson found, about two miles from the first quarry, a few pieces of skull and a lower molar. Luck was playing a big part. So this last discovery served to convince the majority of American scientists and to sow doubt in the minds of the French, the more so because, until very recently, despite our paleontological knowledge, the presence of an ape in England 50,000 years before our era could not be properly explained. And for a very good reason, since the said ape should not have come to England, even as a skeleton, until the beginning of the present century.

For 40 years the quarrel was to continue, giving rise to nearly 300 papers and sometimes involving violent quarrels between experts. One American anthropologist is reported to have said one day that two men who were not among his friends were the Piltdown man! Apart from the petty rivalries of national pride, what was in fact the change that the Piltdown "discovery" brought to prehistory?

When Darwin had shown, in the middle of the last century, that existing animal species derived from animal species that have today disappeared, that the animal world is a connected whole, that at the beginning only the simplest animal forms existed and then had given rise to more complex forms—then, for the first time the theory of evolution experienced a great vogue, even though it had been put forward by Lamarck, a Frenchman, as early as 1809. One of the principal conclusions of all this was that on anatomical and physiological levels man was closely related to the ape. At the end of the last century man was even made to descend directly from the ape. The ideal intermediate creature, the ape-man, had been found in Java in 1890 by a Dutch military doctor, Eugène Dubois. And quite naturally between the ape-man of the Dutch East Indies and real man, another intermediary was sandwiched, a little less ape and a little more man: the Neanderthal man, whose remains had been found at various points in Western Europe, especially in Germany and France, and at Gibraltar.

Thus the ascent of man stood out very clearly. Man and ape (by which must be understood the larger anthropoids, gorillas, orangutans, chimpanzees and gibbons) were second cousins, born of a common stock, and one could trace an imperceptible progression from the common ancestor, a primitive ape, to modern man.

Now into this picture, which is conspicuous for its simplicity, the Piltdown man did not fit at all. This man was reckoned to be about the same age (50,000 to 100,000 years before our time) as the Neanderthal man, but instead of appearing as a composite being, half-man and half-ape, he very paradoxically united the jaw of chimpanzee to the cranium of a modern man. And that was inexplicable, for very good reasons that we now know. So it happened that lively scientific quarrels developed, some scientists clinging to the authenticity of the fossil and therefore determined to refashion their views on the origins of humanity, others denying its authenticity, pointing to the chance union of pieces from two different fossils in the same stratum, and consequently scarcely modifying their ideas on the evolution of prehistoric man.

Thus the Piltdown man stood at the crossroads of various opposing conceptions in human paleontology. And although it is with the story of this fraud that we have begun this book, it is not a matter of chance. The lessons that can already be drawn from it are numerous.

Badly informed by the newspapers, which sacrificed the full scientific story in order to concentrate on a few picturesque details, it seems that the general public, at the end of the year 1953, has scarcely remembered anything but the mistakes of scientists at the hands of an unknown hoaxer. And although some had had a few regrets, it was at not knowing the end of this detective story, since the identity of the forger was uncertain.

Naturally, some people have seen further. They have been stirred by the effect of the fraud on the problem of human origins. The Piltdown man has started something. But the scientists have taken the thing quite well. One might even say that the question is clarified, since an irritating enigma is now solved for better or for worse.

Furthermore, this fraud should draw our attention to the very method which was used to reveal it. It was done by the quantitative analysis of 10 centigrams of bone, in which the presence of a tenth of a milligram of fluorine had to be revealed. These results had then to be confirmed by the very delicate analysis of the nitrogen content of the bones. So we have here an opportunity to emphasize the incomparable help that new physical and chemical techniques are able to bring to the sciences of the past, prehistory and paleontology: a curious anachronism! It is from the most modern scientific techniques, and those requiring great scientific skill to put into practice, that the sciences of the past draw their best results. A recent book, published by a group of prehistorians, is very significant in this respect, for it delves into details of radio-activity, magnetism, microchemistry, X-rays, ultra-violet and infra-red analyses, and the like. The examples given in support of these new methods of investigation are convincing. And the story of the Piltdown hoax is not one of the least of them.

Thus, in short, it is the whole problem of the origins and the evolution of men, animals and plants—that is, the problem of the history of life on the earth—which the Piltdown affair raises. The Coelacanth, that living fossil from Madagascar and the Comoro Islands, gives every reality to these questions.

And is there anyone not interested? Is there anyone who has never asked the exciting question: where do we come from? Paleontology, the science of life on the earth during the completed geological epochs, answers these questions. It answers sometimes with hesitation and sometimes even admits ignorance. Sometimes it is mistaken and has to modify its views as in the case of the Piltdown man; this is not a sign of failure, but, on the contrary, of vitality.

Part One

AT THE CRADLE OF HUMANITY

CHAPTER I

The Customs Officer
and the Academy of Science

WHEN in 1830, after a brilliant career as a student in Paris, a young doctor of some 24 years named Casimir Picard went to settle in Abbeville, no one thought that from this commonplace transfer of a medical practice the science of prehistory would be born in France a few years later. The most eminent English geologists of the nineteenth century were to hold this infant at its baptism.

Abbeville, a sub-prefecture of the Somme department, situated on that river some twelve miles from its estuary, was then one of those quiet little provincial towns of which France has hundreds of examples. With narrow lanes and houses crowding around the gothic cathedral of Saint Vulfran, famous for its splendid façade, it was scarcely different when Casimir Picard went to live there from the humdrum little town that was ravaged by the bombardments of 1940. In Picard's day it was already quite a rich centre, where commerce and industry prospered, thanks to several tanneries and a spinning-mill. Its situation at the mouth of the Somme (the tide was effective to the gates of Abbeville) made of it a lively port and around 1830 work went on busily in the suburb of Hocquet, where the dredgers ceaselessly widened and deepened the canal by which the ships could avoid the elbow described by the Somme as it passes through the town. These dredgers played their part in the birth of the science of prehistory.

Intellectual life was quite bright in Abbeville. In 1797, under the impetus of the chief customs officers, the activities of a certain number of amateur naturalists, archaeologists and antiquaries were centred upon the Abbeville *Société d'émulation*. Casimir Picard, already an eminent naturalist, was immediately welcomed there and soon formed close bonds of friendship with its President,

Jacques Boucher de Perthes, son of the society's founder and himself head of the local customs service. It was to be a fertile friendship. Casimir Picard interested himself especially in paleontological excavations, in the course of which some stones, obviously fashioned by the hand of man, were dug up.

*

As a matter of fact these stones were no novelty. In the Middle Ages, as still happens in our own day, it was not rare for a peasant working in the fields to unearth one of these curiously chipped stones—generally flint—which were called thunderstones. The scientists called them ceraunites, from the Greek word *Keraunos*,

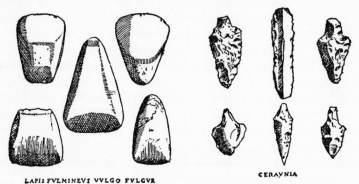

LAPIS FVLMINEVS VVLGO FVLGVR   CERAVNIA

Fig. 1. Thunderstones, or ceraunites, from Mercati's book *Metallotheca Vaticana*.

meaning thunder. In fact, it was then thought that they had been hurled at the earth during storms, or at the very least that their sharp edges resulted from a stroke of lightning. However that may be, from the fact of their comparative rarity great value was attributed to them either as charms or as cures. It would seem, moreover, that such beliefs still persist in some country villages of France and amongst certain primitive tribes.

At the time of the Renaissance, when the majority of the sciences were springing into life (though geology was a late starter) ceraunites were generally regarded as freaks of nature and scientists in the main continued to think of them as the work of lightning. A few alert minds, however, expressed some original ideas on the subject, notably the Italian, Michel Mercati, whose study of thunderstones and fossils was preserved in the Vatican library for two centuries before it was published. In this work, known by the name of *Metallotheca,* posthumously published in the eighteenth century (the author died in 1593), Mercati stated that the thunderstones had in former times been broken off from large flint-nodules and used as weapons.

Actually this idea had already been proposed by several authors of antiquity: Plato, Aristotle, Horace, Pliny, etc., and above all by Lucretius. In his *De Rerum Natura,* he explains that man's first tools were his hands, nails and teeth; later, the branches of trees and stones; then, as a result of the discovery of fire, weapons of bronze and, later still, of iron. Of course, all these authors of Greco-Roman antiquity, who readily borrowed each other's ideas, had no scientific knowledge of the prehistoric remains contained in the earth, but, besides a certain intuition, one has "to give a share either to the persistence of very old traditions or to what was known of savages, or backward peoples, who were numerous on the borders of the then known world," to quote Boule. For in certain circumstances chipped stones have often been used during historical times; for instance, by the Egyptians, who carried out certain ritual incisions on mummies-to-be with the aid of flints, and by the Jews, who used them for circumcision; and by the Etruscans, and therefore by the ancestors of the Romans, who used them to immolate certain sacrificial victims.

Casimir Picard was particularly interested in the problem of ceraunites. He carried out a few excavations himself, but was very busy with his clientele and had often to be content with studying the objects discovered by his colleagues of the *Société d'émulation.* In 1834 and 1835, when reports were presented to members of the Society, he stated several fundamental ideas.

These thunderstones or ceraunites were found in the same strata as the bones of certain animals which one did not expect to find in the sub-soil of Europe: elephants, rhinoceroses and hippopotamuses. The necessary conclusion was that the countryside had not always been as we know it to-day, and also that man had been the contemporary of these now exotic animals.

Moreover, Casimir Picard clearly established that there were two sorts of worked stones. Some had clean, smooth surfaces and had visibly been rubbed for a long time to attain perfect regularity. Others, on the contrary, had a much rougher appearance: detached from a block of flint and rapidly touched up to make their edges sharp, they did not show the finish of the first-mentioned specimens. There had therefore existed two different civilizations, one of chipped stone and the other of polished stone, with which ideas everyone is now vaguely familiar from school history lessons.

Finally, Picard had clearly distinguished that, when striking a flint in order to shape it, the artisans of the first civilizations used sometimes the splinters detached from the crude stone, and at others the crude stone itself, more or less touched up. Casimir Picard thus distinguished two different stone ages.

From the fact that the bones of animals now vanished from Europe and stones indubitably fashioned by man are found in the same geological stratum, we are forced to conclude that:

Europe has not always had a temperate climate, but has in former times enjoyed a warm climate, since elephants, rhinoceroses and hippopotamuses have lived there;

At that epoch men were already living in Europe, and these men, to satisfy their needs, had hunted the elephants, rhinoceroses and hippopotamuses;

These men were little civilized and had only stone tools, the form of these tools making it possible, however, to distinguish several different civilizations.

Such were the principal points established by the researches of Casimir Picard.

*

Although these statements now seem to us too timid, because too general, they were at that time rather unorthodox and ran counter to the opinions of the teachers of geology. Also, they were private and only a few members of the *Société d'émulation* received them. Only the President of the society, Boucher de Perthes, patron and friend of Casimir Picard, was to see them succeed. However, nothing in his character, except his father's example, seemed to predispose Boucher de Perthes to abandon his activities completely in order to devote himself to prehistoric archaeology.

It certainly seems that to begin with this customs officer and poet, this patron of science and near-socialist, this witty writer who could have made an excellent career as a dramatist or songwriter, had been fascinated by the new aspects of the appearance of man on the earth which had been revealed to him. His taste for vast syntheses did the rest and that is why he had to devote the last thirty-one years of his life to prehistoric studies. He died at the age of 80, after having seen the triumph of his own ideas and those of his friend Casimir Picard, who died at the very early age of 35 years.

But this call did not come to Boucher de Perthes at once. If we may use the expression here, he found his road to Damascus when one day in 1835 or 1836 he was superintending the work of a dredger in the Hocquet suburb, beside the canal. The dredger threw up some broken bones, some worked flints, some polished axes, and one axe in particular that had a handle of stag's horn, by which he seems to have been especially moved. These "Celtic antiquities" are described by Casimir Picard. The friendship of Boucher de Perthes for the young doctor was thus cemented and he interested himself more and more in his works on the origin of man. Together they soon worked up some grandiose projects which were much in keeping with their temperaments: the establishment of a local museum, which was to be realized in a few years, also a great plan of excavations in the neighbourhood of Abbeville, with a view to studying systematically all the human antiquities to be found there.

But what sort of man was he, this Jacques Boucher de Crève-coeur de Perthes, recognized everywhere as the father of prehistoric studies?

He was a most attractive person: gentle, calm, and of great tenacity, but never stubborn; sceptical sometimes to the point of contempt, and apt to make fun of an administration which he seems to have entered more by family tradition than by taste. He suffered from rheumatism, but was a confirmed swimmer, and he never ceased to take his daily swim in the Somme up to the age of 76 years! A satirical poet in his leisure hours, this chief customs officer wrote pamphlets in defence of free trade!

Born at Rethel (Ardennes) on September 10th, 1788, his child-hood and youth were spent at Abbeville, where his father had been appointed head of the customs service. We must describe this father in a few words, for Boucher de Perthes was affected to some extent by the family environment in which he lived till he was 16.

The father, a wealthy official, was an enthusiastic naturalist, interesting himself in botany and especially in fossil plants. He was also an amateur of art and archaeology, and transformed his house into a "sanctuary of science and art," as Jacques was to say later, collecting with equal enthusiasm old furniture, ferns, faience and pictures. As a naturalist he was an amateur, certainly, but for his work he was nevertheless elected in 1800 an associate member of the Institut de France. Furthermore, he quickly gathered some amateur investigators around him. Despite the vicissitudes of the revolutionary period which shortly followed his installation at Abbeville, the discussions and researches were fruitful, so that in 1797 Boucher de Crèvecoeur and his friends had founded the *Société d'émulation*. Here were studied all things touching upon science and art, and anyone could apply himself usefully to helping the investigators in their labours. During the nineteenth century the members of this Society were the first to hear of the new ideas that Boucher de Perthes and Casimir Picard propounded concerning the origin of man.

This was the environment in which Jacques Boucher de Perthes was brought up until 1804. In that year he set off on a long journey through Italy. He did not return to Abbeville until 1824, when at the age of 36 years he succeeded his father at the head of the local customs service.

As a matter of fact, until 1837 Boucher de Perthes took very little interest in science generally, and scarcely more in paleontology and archaeology. Of the paternal influence and the atmosphere in which he had been brought up he kept little more than a very lively taste for all antiquities, which he accumulated in his mansion where, at the end of his life, one could move only with difficulty among the most incongruous pieces of furniture, cases of curios and old pictures, all valuable *objets d'art* with the exception of a few notoriously unacceptable fakes. All those who had the good fortune to be able to visit this house before it was destroyed by the bombardments of 1940, could well believe that it had served as a model for Balzac—a contemporary of Boucher de Perthes—when he described the dwellings of nineteenth-century antiquaries in some of his novels.

It required both the ever alert scientific mind and enthusiasm of Casimir Picard to bring Boucher de Perthes to devote himself to prehistoric archaeology. But to understand the full significance of his researches and to demonstrate their novelty, one must know the ideas about the origin of man that ruled in cultured circles at that time, and what was the prevailing view of geologists in particular.

*

Indeed, nobody would then have been advised to contest biblical chronology: the Flood was the essential starting-point from which any system that claimed to explain the origin and evolution of man on the earth should be constructed. That there were some men on our planet before the Flood was a proposition admitted by everyone. But scarcely anyone was concerned to harmonize scientific discoveries with the teachings of the Old Testament. The principal discussions at that time bore upon the exact date of man's creation and the declarations of Archbishop Ussher were readily accepted. According to him, man had been created on March 23rd, 4004 B.C., very precisely, and endless discussions arose as to whether one could confidently accept that date. Everyone, as usual, vigorously defended his own view, but all these controversies have now no more than an anecdotal interest, since they only concern differences of a few centuries.

Furthermore, it was quite shocking to believe that the first human civilizations had made use of stone weapons, since such poverty in the industrial field ran contrary to the easy life offered, by definition, to the inhabitants of the Earthly Paradise. But this was not the view of everyone, and in the eighteenth century Buffon, in his *Epoches de la nature,* spoke of the ceraunites as the "first monuments of the art of man."

Finally, the history of the earth was represented as a series of calm epochs, separated from one another by a series of cataclysms of great violence. During the calm periods, flora and fauna established themselves on the earth, then were remorselessly destroyed during the destruction of the earth's surface marking the end of the period. Buffon thus distinguished seven successive epochs and Cuvier adopted more or less the same opinion. The last cataclysm had been the biblical Flood, and although Adam and Eve, Cain and Abel, and their relatively numerous descendants had lived before this flood, and although Noah himself had survived it, no one thought of being able to find traces of antediluvian man.

These notions were vaguely in the minds of Casimir Picard and Boucher de Perthes. They needed great courage and patience to state that antediluvian man had left traces on the earth.

Boucher de Perthes began by working in close collaboration
with Casimir Picard, meeting the expenses of the excavating work
which he supervised in the young doctor's place, since the latter
was busy with his patients. When Casimir Picard died at the age
of 35, in 1841, Boucher de Perthes continued with the excavations alone, and more eagerly than ever.

In the summer of 1844, during some digging at the site of the
hospital, close to his port, he himself made discoveries in the presence of two of his colleagues so that there was not the least possibility of fraud: in the same stratum, between July 23rd and
August 26th, he found a chipped flint, three chipped axes and a
large fragment of an elephant's molar tooth. This passed all
bounds! The proof of the existence of "antediluvian" man was
there, and also the proof that this man, using tools of stone, had
been the contemporary of the great exotic beasts that have now
disappeared from Europe. Boucher de Perthes at once advised the
Paris museum. They remained sceptical. Only Brongniart, the
paleobotanist and friend of his father, gave any encouragement.
But this was of little consequence to Boucher de Perthes. Definitely convinced of the importance and truth of his theories, he
fought to get them accepted by the scientific world and eventually
won a victory against great odds.

He drafted the manuscript of *Antiquités celtiques et antédi-
luviennes* and sent it to the Institut de France in 1846, accompanied by a letter requesting that a commission of enquiry should
be appointed to come and examine his discoveries. A commission of
five members was actually named, but it never went to Abbeville.
The same year, Boucher de Perthes wrote to the director of the
museum at Flourens to offer him his collection of stone implements. He never received a reply.

In 1847 he repeated his offer, this time to the Institut, which
emphatically refused it. In fact, at the Academy of Science the
permanent secretary, Elie de Beaumont, a geologist, exercised a
preponderant influence: he refused to believe that it was possible
for man and elephant to be contemporary: furthermore, he claimed
that the chipped flints were of Roman origin. Of what consequence
in the eyes of these Paris gentlemen were the eccentric theories
of a little provincial amateur as opposed to the authoritative opinion
of the greatest of French geologists?

But all of a sudden events moved with a rush. An amateur

archaeologist and naturalist of Amiens, Dr. Rigollot, who had been told of the theories of Boucher de Perthes, journeyed to Abbeville with the firm intention of demonstrating the absurdity of these ideas. He came, but he went away convinced that Boucher de Perthes was right; he undertook in his turn to excavate the gravel-pits at Saint-Acheul, a suburb of Amiens on the banks of the Somme. In 1834 he published a *Report on the Chipped Flint Implements Found at Saint-Acheul, near Amiens, Considered in Their Geological and Archaeological Relations;* in this it was clearly demonstrated that these stone objects were found in the same gravel beds as the bones of elephant, rhinoceros and hippopotamus.

All this created a great stir, more especially as Boucher de Perthes had not remained inactive and had published more papers and pamphlets to make his discoveries known. Elie de Beaumont, however, remained unmoved and uncompromising. But some English experts, who had been aroused and were less mulish than the members of the Institut de France, decided to go and see things on the spot. It was a fine delegation that arrived at the banks of the Somme on April 26th, 1859: among them was a man of world reputation, one of the greatest of English scientists and the most eminent British geologist of the nineteenth century, Charles Lyell; with him were Falconer the paleontologist, Prestwich the stratigrapher, John Evans the young and already very brilliant archaeologist, and Flower, the anatomist. These were men whose reputation and scientific honesty were incontestable.

Boucher de Perthes had them visit his excavations and showed them his collections. From Abbeville they went on to Amiens, where Dr. Rigollot was proud to show them round the gravel-pits of Saint-Acheul. They saw, they dug, they discussed, and they went away convinced of the exactness of the theses maintained by Boucher de Perthes and Rigollot. In a few weeks Lyell drafted a report which appeared at the end of 1859 and fell like a bomb into French scientific circles.

Meanwhile, other members of the English delegation had undertaken excavations on the banks of the Thames: they made discoveries identical with those made on the banks of the Somme. Others had re-read old reports and saw that during the preceding hundred years a number of discoveries like those made by Boucher de Perthes had been reported but had passed unnoticed.

This is not the place to deal at length with the works of those earlier discoverers, who do not seem to have had either the knowledge or the conviction necessary to assure the acceptance of their ideas. It is not unprofitable, however, to record their names and relate a few picturesque items from that early period.

About 1690 a London pharmacist, Conyers, found in the gravel bed of an abandoned arm of the Thames a pointed chipped flint close to the almost complete skeleton of an elephant. A friend of Conyers reported the fact to the Society of Antiquaries in London and explained that it was an elephant of the Roman army of the Emperor Claudius, killed by a Briton. In the middle of the eighteenth century, Thomsen and Worsaal, who were Danes, established that in certain parts of their country three civilizations had followed one another: at first there was a stone age, then a bronze age, and finally an iron age. The relics of these civilizations were found in the superimposed geological beds, the most recent of them being naturally closest to the surface.

More interesting was the discovery made in 1797 by John Frere, at Hoxne, in Norfolk: in a pit where the raw material for brickmaking was being dug, he found, at a depth of 12 feet, some chipped flints mixed with the remains of large animals. He attributed them to a very ancient period of human history, a period when the use of metal was unknown.

In France, in 1823, Ami Boué presented Cuvier with a human humerus taken from the banks of the Rhine together with animal remains. But Cuvier denied the possibility that the two finds were the same age. However, similar discoveries were about to follow one another rapidly, showing the presence side by side in the same stratum of the bones of animals that have now vanished and human relics, either in the form of chipped stones or bones. These discoveries were made in France (Jouannet, in Dordogne, 1815; de Cristol, near Montpellier, 1829, etc.), in England (McEnnery, at Kent's Hole, near Torquay, where the English investigators, convinced by Lyell, were later to return), and in Belgium. In Belgium it was Dr. P. C. Schmerling who, in several caves in the Liège region in 1829, found chipped flints mixed with the bones of mammoth, rhinoceros, hyena and bear, as well as human skulls; in 1833 and 1834 he published two large volumes on these researches and declared that the stone implements were the work of prehistoric man.

In France, between 1826 and 1829, a pharmacist named Tournal,

Edouard Lartet.

Jacques Boucher de Perthes.

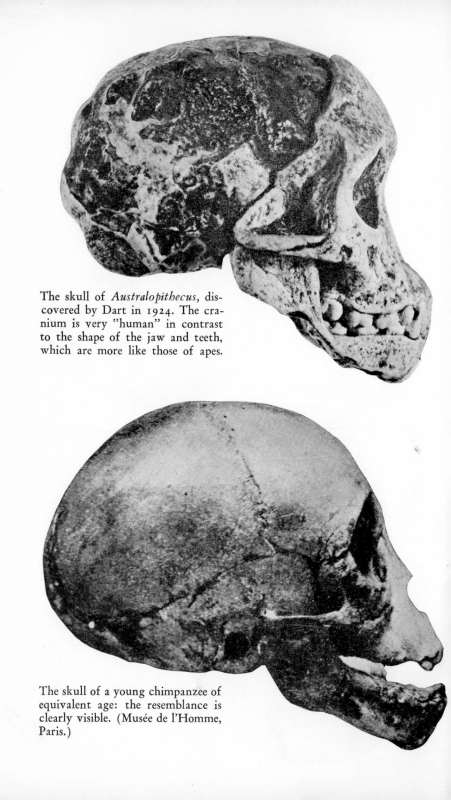

The skull of *Australopithecus*, discovered by Dart in 1924. The cranium is very "human" in contrast to the shape of the jaw and teeth, which are more like those of apes.

The skull of a young chimpanzee of equivalent age: the resemblance is clearly visible. (Musée de l'Homme, Paris.)

keeper of the museum at Narbonne, had also, like Schmerling, realized the importance of the discoveries he had made in the cave at Bise (Aude). There he found, alongside human remains, fragments of pottery, bones of animals missing from our present fauna, and—this was the most striking discovery—a certain number of engraved reindeer bones.

*

Despite the tribute we have just paid to the forerunners of Casimir Picard and Boucher de Perthes, we must nevertheless emphasize the merits of these two, who alone were not content to realize the importance of their discoveries but had also exploited them to the utmost. Now that Lyell's publication had shaken the Academy of Science things moved quickly. Young and unknown at that time, but later accepted as one of the greatest of French paleontologists, Albert Gaudry came to Saint-Acheul in 1859. He never left the workers on their own and so prevented any possibility of fraud. He found the classic association once again: nine chipped axes, the teeth of a large bull and various hippopotamus, elephant and rhinoceros bones. This time, the discovery was published in the reports of the Academy of Science (meeting of October 3rd, 1859).

Nevertheless, the recognized authorities remained sceptical. Such stubbornness began to turn to their discredit. Their errors of judgment were many. A note by Lartet on "the geological antiquity of the human species in Western Europe" was rejected in 1860. The publication by Boucher de Perthes, in the same year, of a work entitled *De l'homme antédiluvien et de ses oeuvres* was ignored. In 1860 again, the discoveries made by Gosse, a Genevese, and Lamotte-Picquet, a Frenchman, in the gravel-pits of Grenelle (Paris) were treated with scorn. And on May 18th, 1863, at the Academy of Science, the all too permanent secretary, Elie de Beaumont, again declared: "I do not believe that the human species was contemporaneous with the *Elephas primigenius*. In this respect I continue to share M. Cuvier's opinion. M. Cuvier's opinion is a work of genius; it has not been destroyed."

Cuvier's opinion, to which constant reference was made, carried great weight. This French scientist must truly be regarded as the founder of comparative anatomy. Moreover, he was the first to recognize the real nature of a great number of fossils, and for this

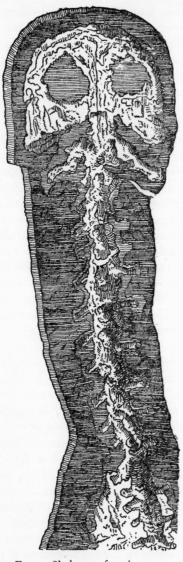

FIG. 2. Skeleton of a giant salamander, long thought to be the skeleton of a prehistoric man.

reason must be placed in the ranks of the pioneers of animal paleontology. However, faced with Elie de Beaumont's appeal to the authority of Cuvier when faced with so many proofs of the existence of prehistoric man, there are some observations that must be made.

Cuvier died, in fact, in 1832 and knew nothing of the work of Casimir Picard, Boucher de Perthes or the English geologists. In using Cuvier's theory to deny categorically discoveries that took place more than 30 years after his death, Elie de Beaumont, to whom in the end we owe no single important discovery, certainly appears to have done great harm to the posthumous reputation of Cuvier. Moreover, Cuvier had never had much luck with the prehistoric human bones that were given him—or those that claimed to be such. Sometimes, in fact, the specimens proved to be the bones of turtles or whales, sometimes the remains of elephants, and on another occasion the skeleton turned out to be that of a salamander. On the other hand, when they were indisputably the remains of a human being, it was always impossible to date with certainty the strata from which they had been taken.

Finally, it should not be forgotten that Cuvier, a firm believer in the system of successive cataclysms that had convulsed the surface of the earth at more or less regular intervals, thus causing the flora and fauna to disappear radically, had once written that "before the last revolution man was able to inhabit the earth, in some not very extensive region, from where a few individuals had repopulated the planet, while the bones of all the others, having perished together in the cataclysm, were covered by the sea."

And who knows, had Cuvier lived long enough and had the chance to study the reports of Casimir Picard, Boucher de Perthes and Dr. Rigollot, as well as Lyell's work, he might once again have said what he once wrote to his collaborator, Duméril, "My dear friend, we are mistaken."

On the other hand, we must recognize that in the writings of Boucher de Perthes everything recorded should not be regarded as valid coin. Very often he was misled by his workmen, who in the hope of reward were ingenious in getting him to find "Celtic" objects. It was easier for these labourers to go and collect some polished flints on the plateau where the Picardy plain reaches the edge of the Channel and then to bury them in a suitable spot. Similarly, when in 1863 Boucher de Perthes discovered the famous Moulin-Quignon jaw-bone in the environs of Abbeville, he allowed himself to be fooled as to its authenticity, for it was later proved that the bone was stolen from a nearby charnel-house. Finally, the prehistorian Vayson tells this very picturesque tale: one of his cousins, Mme. Ducatel, had spent her youth at Abbeville, and during her walks she had been much intrigued by the work of a peasant who was spending his time in smashing stones on the paving-blocks of the road; she questioned him one day and got this reply: "I am making prehistoric axes for M. Boucher de Perthes." Also, among the flint-nodules which he had gathered and which, it was claimed, had been worked, there were some which were certainly "worked," but not by the hand of man; these nodules were the work of running water or some other erosion agent, which had polished them by rubbing them one against the other. This did not prevent Boucher de Perthes, lacking for once in critical spirit, from regarding them as objects of worship, the famous "stone figures," which he described with some complacency.

However, before he died on August 2nd, 1868, Boucher de

Perthes had the satisfaction of seeing the triumph of his and his young friend Casimir Picard's ideas on the antiquity of man on the earth. He had the further satisfaction of seeing created a group of scholars who were about to turn prehistoric studies into a science, the inspiration of which was essentially French, often assisted, as he himself was, by the labours of English experts.

*

The French prehistorians at the end of the nineteenth century are too numerous even to consider mentioning them all. However, it would be unjust not to make mention here of Dr. Hamy, of Quatrefages, of Edouard Piette, the great explorer of Pyrenean caves, of Capitan, Cartailhac, and Gabriel de Mortillet, who, appointed assistant-keeper of the Museum of National Antiquities at St. Germain, started in 1864 the first prehistory review and later published, in collaboration with his son Adrien, those two basic works *Musé préhistorique* and *Préhistorique*. Marcellin Boule, the Abbé Breuil, Denis Peyrony, etc.—are all our contemporaries. But one name overshadows all others, a name that we must place on the same level as Boucher de Perthes: Edouard Lartet (1801–1871).

Justice of the Peace in a little straggling village of Gers, he lived for 30 years without taking the least interest in the world of geology, paleontology or archaeology. Very erudite, he read a great deal and spent his leisure hours and weekends on his father's lands, interesting himself in their exploitation, in cattle-rearing and in work on the soil. One day, about 1830, a peasant showed him a very strange tooth which had been dug out of a field a few days earlier. It was the tooth of a mastodon, first cousin to the modern elephant, which once lived in Europe and which Cuvier was the first to describe. No more was needed to move Lartet profoundly: to discover for oneself or to examine on the spot the remains of living creatures that have disappeared thousands of years ago is something that very few can resist. Lartet could not resist the attraction of a mastodon's molar. He devoured the works of Cuvier and learned all he could of zoology, anatomy and osteology. He undertook excavations around his property and in 1834 discovered the famous Sansan bed; from it he extracted a fossil ape, which was given the name of *Pliopithecus,* and he later found other paleological treasures at the same place.

In 1850 he was in Paris at the paleological laboratory of the

Museum, where he was preparing a great study of fossil Proboscidea (elephants, mammoths, mastodons, etc.), which appeared in 1859. Meanwhile he made two important discoveries. One was at Sansan, of a further fossil ape, *Dryopithecus*, cousin to *Pliopithecus*; these two will be studied at greater length in the next chapter, in their place as more or less direct ancestors of the human branch.

The other discovery took place at the large village of Aurignac in the Haute-Garonne, where an inquisitive inhabitant one day overturned the slab that covered the entrance to a small cave. In it he found a number of human skeletons. Lartet was summoned; his reputation in the district was beginning to grow. They were anxious to remove the skeletons to the cemetery in order to give them Christian burial. Lartet arrived in haste, dug and found in the middle of the geological bed in which the skeletons lay the remains of hearths, bones, chipped flints, and the more or less broken bones of reindeer, bears, rhinoceroses and hyenas. He concluded that these were the remains of a funerary feast. Lartet was not wrong in thinking that all burials, whether prehistoric or modern, are always accompanied by suitable feasting, but he was mistaken in thinking that he had found bones from the polished stone age and on industries and fossil bones from the chipped stone age. However, this spurred him on to dig carefully in several other Pyrenean caves and to report his discoveries in a paper on "the geological antiquity of the human species in Western Europe," which was rejected by the Academy of Science but enthusiastically received by English and Swiss scientific societies.

Soon, Lartet received from Eyzies (Dordogne) a small box containing specimens analogous to those which he had just discovered at Aurignac, accompanied by a letter advising him that the region was full of similar remains. He delayed only long enough to call for his English friend, Henry Christy, before beginning in 1863 a campaign of excavations in the valley of the Vézère. Lartet's special discovery was the irrefutable proof of the co-existence of man and the great mammals in the form of the mammoth engraved on a mammoth tusk in the La Madeleine cave.

Lartet was luckier than Boucher de Perthes. In 1869 he was appointed Professor of Paleontology at the Museum, but he died shortly afterwards at the age of 70 years without having been able, because of the Franco-Prussian war, to give his first lesson.

So three names should be remembered: Casimir Picard, Jacques Boucher de Perthes and Edouard Lartet, who were by different rights the real founders of the science of prehistory. To these the name of an English geologist, Charles Lyell, should be added because of his clear-sightedness: his scientific authority powerfully helped the acceptance of the ideas of these three founders. Although these latter may often have set out on mistaken hypotheses, when they had sometimes worked on manifestly false objects, they

FIG. 3. Mammoth engraved on mammoth bone, discovered by Lartet at La Madeleine in 1864.

demonstrated the indisputable existence of antediluvian—or prehistoric—man.

*

But it is to Lartet that we must give the credit of having been the first to trace in a systematic way the framework within which the evolution of humanity proceeded. In fact, throughout this evolution the climates changed, the landscapes were transformed, the animals and the plans were not always the same, certain species died out and others made their appearance, and some may have migrated from one country to another as a result of climatic changes. It was in 1866 that Lartet was able to sketch out a first chronology of prehistoric times on the following lines. For some time the archaeologists had already recognized that on the surface of the earth, at least in Europe, there has been three successive epochs: the Stone Age, of which evidence had been provided by Boucher de Perthes, the Bronze Age and the Iron Age. Lartet, starting from the same principles, was able to put forward the following sub-divisions for the Stone Age: the age of the great cave bear, the age of elephant and rhinoceros, the Reindeer Age, and finally the age of the aurochs.

This classification was therefore based on paleontological characteristics: the study of the fauna and, by implication, of the climates. It was a very similar classification to that reached by Boucher de Perthes without, however, his being able to expatiate upon it: in the following order he distinguished a tropical period (elephant and rhinoceros), a glacial period (reindeer) and a temperate period (aurochs). Other classifications were suggested in rapid succession by de Mercey in 1875 and by the Mortillets. But it was not until the first writings of Marcellin Boule in 1888 that we had at last a firm chronological framework, established upon indisputable data, of the 500 millennia which have seen the human species conquer the entire world.

Boule showed clearly that three different kinds of data could be used to fix this chronology. They must be studied separately before attempting their coherent synthesis. First of all comes the data provided by archaeological studies. Thus the study of weapons and tools (known as typology) permits us to establish the fact that there was first an age of chipped stone, followed by an age of polished stone; certainly, this indication is a very rough one, but it permits us to divide prehistoric times into three successive periods: the old stone or chipped stone age, known scientifically as the Paleolithic (that is "Old Stone"), then an intermediate period, forming the transition between a hunting and an agricultural civilization, known as the Mesolithic, and finally the polished stone age, characterized especially by the invention of agriculture, of stock-raising and pottery, known as the Neolithic ("New Stone"). Archaeology also informs us of the manner in which the civilizations followed one another and shows us that the crudely worked tools were gradually replaced by other tools which were progressively finer and more varied as prehistoric time went by.

Nevertheless, these archaeological classifications should not be accepted blindly, for in the same epoch all the people scattered over the surface of the earth were not necessarily at the same stage of evolution and did not necessarily use the same tools or the same weapons. One has only to think of how future archaeologists will have to study the civilizations of the middle of the twentieth century, taking account of the co-existence in space of the industrial civilizations of Europe and America, using atomic power, and quite primitive civilizations, like that of the pygmies of Central Africa, using wooden weapons, or that of the Motiron Indians of South America. Archaeological evidence alone will never allow one to state that two prehistoric civilizations were contemporary because they used the same types of tools.

We must also take into consideration the fact that two different groups of humans, completely separated in time and space, can create similar tools, for there are not many ways of cutting stone. The prehistorian, Jacques de Morgan, has clearly emphasized this fault of "the experts who seek to link up civilizations that are very remote from one another as if there had been a Cook's office at that time to enable peoples to go on some extraordinary excursions."

However, the study of typology permits us to distinguish three divisions of the Paleolithic Age, corresponding to the degree of perfection in the stone-cutting techniques that it reveals and by the increasingly great diversity of the implements. This age of chipped stone begins with the crude tools of the Lower Paleolithic, continues with the finer and more varied tools of the Middle Paleolithic, and ends with the very numerous types of tools in stone and bone of the Upper Paleolithic, which further saw the birth of art. To study these diverse types of implements in greater detail, the technique of their manufacture, as well as the works of art painted and engraved by the men of the Reindeer Age, will be the object of a later chapter.

In this way, therefore, archaeology allows us to establish a relative chronology, and (for a given region) to establish the order of civilizations which followed one another there. But Boule has shown that other information can and should be used—that provided by geology and by the particular branch known as paleontology. The geologist teaches the anthropologist and archaeologist that during prehistoric times several very cold periods succeeded one another, in the course of which the glaciers, creeping down the mountains, more or less covered the surrounding plateaus and plains. These glaciers have left the traces of their passage in the form of stone trails, called moraines, pushed up in front or along the sides of the glacier and abandoned where they stood on the

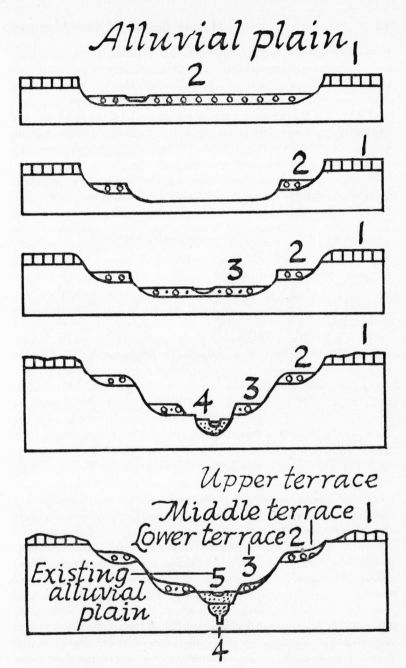

FIG. 4. Sketch of the formation of hanging river terraces.

retreat of the ice, consequent upon a general warming up. Thus we can settle the boundaries of the habitable territory at a given epoch, also by dating more or less exactly the age of the glaciation, determine the age of other geological sites that were contemporaneous with it and contain the remains of human industries. Furthermore, the enlargement of the glaciers, by mobilizing the available water upon the earth's surface, led to a general lowering of the sea level; this resulted in an increase in the excavating work of the rivers, since their beds have always the tendency to sink into the soil in order to approach the level of the sea. Thus the beaches and the hanging terraces at the edge of the sea, or on the banks of

FIG. 5. Prehistoric fauna as seen by prehistoric man: woolly rhinoceros wounded by arrows. (La Colombière, Dordogne.)

the rivers of the plain, bear witness to the discontinuous succession of glacial periods. It is in such terraces, on the banks of the Somme, that Boucher de Perthes discovered his first chipped stone implements.

Finally, these geological and climatic changes were attended by changes in the fauna and flora of the different countries. Thus paleontology provides the prehistorian with a third source of information for setting up a chronology of prehistoric times. The succession is clearly marked by a fauna called warm (elephants, Merck rhinoceroses, hippopotamuses); then by a fauna called cold, corresponding to three or four glaciations which then covered Europe (mammoths, hairy rhinoceroses, reindeer); and finally by a temperate fauna, very similar to the fauna of Europe to-day.

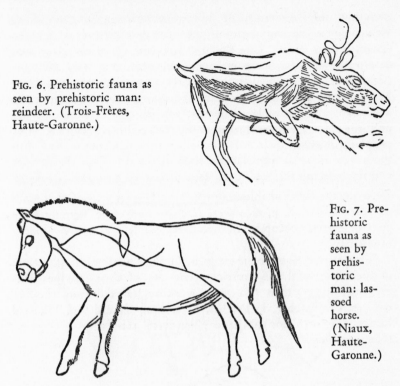

FIG. 6. Prehistoric fauna as seen by prehistoric man: reindeer. (Trois-Frères, Haute-Garonne.)

FIG. 7. Prehistoric fauna as seen by prehistoric man: lassoed horse. (Niaux, Haute-Garonne.)

The warm fauna corresponds approximately to the beginning of the Lower Paleolithic, the cold fauna to the Middle and Upper Paleolithic, the temperate fauna to the Mesolithic and Neolithic.

If agreement is to-day more or less unanimous so far as concerns the relative chronology of prehistoric times—that is, if the experts are no longer in serious dispute, except on points of detail, in regard to the contemporaneity or the succession of one civilization with respect to another in any given bed—agreement is far from being so perfect where absolute chronology is concerned. In fact one would very much like to be able to fix the age of a given skeleton with certainty, or of a given worked stone or a work of art; this is, indeed, what most interests the layman. The matter is unfortunately very difficult, although recent physicochemical methods have brought some degree of accuracy. These methods will be set out at greater length in a later chapter, for they concern not only the study of prehistory but equally the general chronology of the history of life. It will be sufficient, in order to fix one's ideas, to say here that the Paleolithic Age began, at least in our Western European countries, approximately 400,000 years before our era and ended only 10,000 years ago; the Mesolithic age, covering 3,000 or 4,000 years, ended on an average about 5,000 years ago, and was replaced by the Neolithic Age (copper, bronze and iron), a stage of evolution at which certain so-called primitive peoples still exist.

*

Thus, contrary to the view that is too widespread, the Gauls were not the first inhabitants of France. Several tens of thousands of years before them, men were already there, who, coming from Asia or Africa, occupied European regions left vacant by glacial invasions.

What do we know of these men, of their anatomical structure, of their industrial and artistic activity, or of their religious conceptions? In less than 100 years, working forward from the discoveries of Boucher de Perthes, of Casimir Picard and Edouard Lartet, the prehistorians have given very satisfying answers to these questions.

Fig. 8. Prehistoric fauna as seen by prehistoric man: male bison. (La Grèze, Dordogne.)

CHAPTER II

The Hunt for Fossil Man

AFTER Boucher de Perthes had found the prehistoric stone tools and duly proved their origin and antiquity, he naturally would not rest until he had found the remains of the men who had made them. Now that the working implements of fossil man were known, it should surely be possible to find out what that man was like, and eventually in 1863 Boucher de Perthes was in possession of his fossil man in person, if one can so describe a very fine half of a jaw-bone in a very good state of preservation, found not far from Abbeville in the Moulin-Quignon quarry.

Several months earlier Boucher de Perthes had promised the then considerable sum of 200 francs to any man who should find a fossil bone in the quarries then being worked. At that time a first-class excavation laborer received a maximum of 2.50 francs a day. It might be said that in the Abbeville region, as well as around Amiens, excavation work became very attractive after Boucher de Perthes had revealed the existence of prehistoric axes. To Boucher de Perthes himself an axe was sold for five sous, because he was a local man and was much liked by his workmen. But other geologists and lay visitors had to pay 10 or 15 sous, and the English 20 sous or more. In these circumstances, given that with some skill a flint already worked by natural geological causes could be transformed in a few hours into a very acceptable axe, a fair number of workmen formed the habit of making stone tools themselves and, according to the importance of the visitor, arranged their discovery in the quarry itself or sold them in the nearest village. But the sum of 200 francs was incomparably more attractive than such small sources of profit.

Although Boucher de Perthes was too intelligent not to have known of these practices, he maintained a blind confidence in the discoveries made by his diggers, whom he knew very well and it is by no means certain that he did not, in his own heart and with some malice, approve of their astuteness when they acquired some extra money at the expense of the idlers. Unfortunately, his too great confidence in his workmen was grossly abused in respect of the Moulin-Quignon jaw-bone. In fact, a short time after he had made the promise of 200 francs reward for the discovery of the first bones of antediluvian man—on March 23rd, 1863, to be precise—Boucher de Perthes was led to discover in rapid succession, first two human teeth, then half a jaw-bone, then a third tooth and finally a fourth tooth from which a few fragments were missing.

In 1863 Boucher de Perthes was 75 years old. For 25 years he had struggled almost alone against all the learned men of France to get the existence of prehistoric man accepted. His theories and deductions had been recognized and proclaimed valid by English scholars only three years before. So this discovery of human teeth and a jaw-bone seemed to him, as well as to his friends and supporters, the crowning of a brilliant scientific career. Advised at once, his English friends hurried to Abbeville a second time. The matter was important. This time it was no longer a question of studying the tools of prehistoric man, but of making acquaintance with this prehistoric man himself. However, some of the most eminent among the English specialists returned to London much less convinced by the mandible and teeth than they had been four years earlier by the "Celtic" axes. Some days later Falconer, the paleontologist, published a short report to show that one of the molars given him by Boucher de Perthes was of very recent origin because chemical analysis showed that it was very rich in protein; he also showed that the stone tools found in the same Moulin-Quignon bed were fakes, having been deliberately cut. From this it was only a step to conclude that the jaw-bone itself was not authentic and Falconer did not hesitate to take that step. By a curious reversal, the French, who had ignored or ridiculed Boucher de Perthes for 25 years, took up the cudgels on his behalf and accused the English scientists of partiality, ignorance, chauvinism, jealousy and many other even more amiable things. The affair developed very quickly. Tempers ran high. Some Englishmen challenged Falconer's too categorical statements. The Press seized upon the Moulin-Quignon jaw-bone and, aided by increasingly tendentious arguments, turned it into a philosophical and religious problem and succeeded only in heaping confusion on confusion.

In the end, a little more than a month after the discovery, a mixed Anglo-French commission, comprising the most qualified experts of both countries, established that the Moulin-Quignon jaw-bone was authentic. It was the Dean of the science faculty in Paris himself, the celebrated zoologist Milne-Edwards, President of the commission, who submitted the report to the Academy of Science on May 18th, 1863. In France the matter was regarded as closed and, apart from a few retrograde minds, everyone agreed that prehistoric man had at last surrendered his remains to the one who deserved most to find them.

On the other hand, in London the polemics continued worse than ever. In June two of the scientists who went to Abbeville in 1859 to authenticate Boucher de Perthe's discoveries exchanged acrimonious letters. Evans, the young archaeologist, set himself up against Prestwich, the geologist. Finally, the English experts agreed to send a professional digger named Keeping to work in the same Moulin-Quignon quarry. He had already proved himself under their direction in various English beds. Keeping reached Boucher de Perthes on June 2nd, 1863, and worked there for four months. Quite determined to get his jaw-bone authenticated, Boucher de Perthes welcomed him in a very friendly fashion. But when on his return to London, after having continuously replied "good, good" to Boucher de Perthes, who did not understand a word of English, Keeping declared that there had been a fraud, Boucher de Perthes felt that his self-esteem had been a little wounded. As for the English, a letter from John Evans, published in the *Athenaeum* of July 4th, 1863, put an end to the debate.

Taking his stand on Keeping's statements, Evans resumed certain arguments from his earlier letters. He demonstrated that the shaped stone tools discovered at the same time as the jaw-bone were fakes because the dark sandy matrix in which they were enveloped was quite recent and could easily be washed off with water, and that with very little trouble the finger-prints of the diggers could be revealed on them; because the flints themselves, freed from their matrix, did not show the usual patina of very old flints; because, bluntly, at Moulin-Quignon they had begun to discover chipped axes in great abundance when they had been very rare a few months before the discovery of the jaw-bone; because, finally, a minute analysis made it possible to reveal traces of iron on the surface of these flints that came from the tool used to shape them. Keeping himself had, on two or three occasions, set traps for the workers, who had allowed themselves to be caught. One day a digger drew his attention to the presence of a prehistoric tool when, by leaning forward so as to conceal the position of the axe, Keeping alone could have seen it. On another day he noticed that a certain fissure in the quarry had been filled up during the night; digging in it the next morning, he found a stone implement 3 feet down and noticed that beyond it the fissure continued just as he had seen it the day before. Many other arguments were brought forward by Evans, who ended his letter with the sincere hope that the Moulin-Quignon jaw-bone would be relegated to oblivion.

Another fraud! It is not—alas!—the last that will be recorded in this book. For fraud is easy in prehistoric archaeology, so easy that a famous specialist, Vayson de Pradenne, was able to devote a book of nearly 700 pages to its study. However, fraud often has no other motive than interest. It is almost certain that if Boucher de Perthes had not been so generous to his workers he would not have discovered the Moulin-Quignon jaw-bone so "fortuitously." This is one of the principal difficulties that the prehistorian encounters in his quest for fossil man. If he does not interest the layman in his works—and how can he interest him except by money?—he risks losing very precious pieces for ever through negligence or malevolence. But on the other hand there is a great temptation for the workers at a digging to create the bones or shaped stones which will assure substantial profits; a little skill, average intelligence and an observant mind are sufficient for making fakes that are more than passable, at times so successfully that the experts are deceived for several years. It must not be forgotten that the Piltdown fraud, probably the most resounding of all paleontological frauds, was not revealed for 40 years, and then only by the use of very delicate physico-chemical tests which were devised only a short while ago. Let it suffice to insist on the extreme scientific strictness with which every prehistorian and every archaeologist has to receive a new item, and to emphasize the difficulty of their task by showing the trouble they take in procuring new material. One does not create an animal or a plant still unknown to the zoologist or the botanist. But fraud is easy, on the other hand, when a bone fragment, a shaped stone or a picture at the far end of a cave is concerned.

Without going as far as fraud, the method of recompense can have other inconveniences, though certainly minor ones. Thus in Java, in 1937, the Dutch geologist von Koenigswald was presented in a few days, by the greater number of his laborers, with fragments of bone from the skull of a man-ape. The clearly recent fractures in these fragments attracted his attention; in fact, the skull, which had been discovered intact, had provided an opportunity for an original operation in the multiplication of rewards by the simple process of breaking it up into many parts. In the end, however, the incident was more amusing than serious, for the freshness of the fractures made possible an easy reconstitution of the whole of the skull.

*

The first fossil skull to arouse any interest in scientific circles was the one discovered in 1856 in the Feldhofer cave, between Düsseldorf and Elberfeld in the side of a ravine called the Neanderthal. Actually, only the top of the cranium was discovered; it had been very nearly destroyed by the quarry-men working on the banks of the Düssel, but luckily came into the hands of Dr. Fühlrott. Soon a detailed description appeared in a German scientific review under the name of the renowned paleontologist, Schaaffhausen. To-day one can hardly imagine the emotion that gripped scientific circles during the next 10 years. Coming immediately after Boucher de Perthes' discoveries and the publication of Darwin's book, this skull constituted for some the remains of a very venerable ancestor of man, while for others, opposed to the evolutionist ideas of the English, saw nothing that deserved special attention. For one of the greatest experts in pathological anatomy of the nineteenth century, a German named Virchow, the skull was that of a diseased person. The fact is that, being very thick and quite abnormally shaped, with a bony ridge above the orbits, a flattening of the top of the head that is not found in any modern man, and a bony ridge at the nape, this fragment of skull was truly odd. Gibb, the Englishman, went further: he bluntly diagnosed disease and demonstrated, with the aid of unanswerable arguments, that it was a case of hypertrophic osteitis.

Another Englishman identified this cranium as that of an idiot afflicted with rickets; upon which, but, of course, without any malice, the French anthropologist Pruner-Bey stated that the skull was quite identical with that of a modern Irishman. Finally, to crown everything, Mayer, a German, was persuaded that he had found the last word in the story by demonstrating that the relic was that of a Cossack killed during the anti-Napoleonic campaign of 1814.

Meanwhile, others had slightly saner ideas. A modest English anatomist, Dr. King, whose name deserves to be handed down to

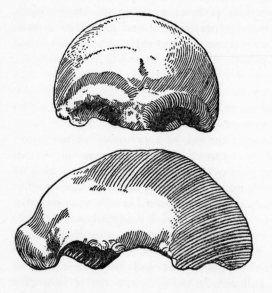

FIG. 9. The top of the Neanderthal skull. Four typical features are clearly visible: the thickness of the bone, the ridge above the orbits and the occipital ridge, and the flattening of the summit.

posterity, saw in it an authentic ancestor of the human species and created for this much disputed piece of bone a species and a style all its own: *Homo neanderthalensis.* After a very carefully conducted study, Huxley, Darwin's faithful lieutenant, stated that this was a real man, but a more primitive man than that existing to-day. Bishop Wilberforce, who ventured to contradict him and to cast doubts on the antiquity of the origins of the human species, drew upon himself the retort that it would be better to be a perfected ape than a degenerate Adam. But during the years that followed, Huxley became hesitant: at one time he stated in his writings that the Neanderthal cranium had belonged to a creature clearly intermediate between ape and man, and at another time he considered it very improbable that the skull was that of the much-sought intermediary. More cautious still, in 1871 Darwin spoke of it at length in his work on the origins of man, but did not reach any conclusion.

It must be admitted that there is some reason for such hesitation when placed in the climate of the time and when the ideas that ruled in geology and paleontology between 1860 and 1870 are taken into consideration. Also, it was difficult to base an irrefutable argument on a piece of skull. It would have been necessary to discover a whole skeleton, but this skeleton was only discovered some 50 years later, in 1908, in the south of France. Furthermore, the Neanderthal cranium had not been found *in situ* in a well-defined bed, but had only been received after the event and the workers had not been able to point out its position with reasonable precision. Finally, it was very rash at that time to assert the close kinship of apes and men and the most convinced partisans of this kinship, among the foremost of whom was Huxley, were somewhat justified in their caution.

However, rather by chance and probably also because men's minds were interested by the new theories of Boucher de Perthes and Darwin, the discoveries of bones were not long in multiplying. In 1864 the meeting of the British Association was shown a fossil head identical with the one from the Neanderthal, but possessing the greater part of the face and jaw. This head had been completely forgotten for nearly 20 years in a store-room of the British Museum. In 1866, at La Naulette, not far from Liège, a lower jaw of very primitive appearance was dug up in a cave. Finally, once again in Belgium, in a cave at Spy, near Namur, the Belgian geologists de Puydt and Lohest in 1866 discovered the remains of three men, two almost intact skulls and some limb bones, mixed with animal bones and tools of the Mousterian epoch. This time the antiquity of the bones was absolutely beyond dispute. In fact, the bones had been discovered, as geologists say, *"in situ"*; that is, they had been got out of the soil of the cave instead of being brought along by some amateur or layman after having passed through a number of hands. From this fact it was easy to fix a relative age to these human remains in accordance with the geological stratum that contained them. Furthermore, animal remains had been found beside them that came from a cold fauna—mammoths and woolly rhinoceroses. These remains were described very minutely and very definitely resembled the Neanderthal cranium. Unfortunately, at this time this ancestor of man— or what was claimed as such—had difficulty in finding his place in the museums and in the papers of the experts.

At last it certainly seemed that we were faced with creatures that had lived 75,000 years ago in the Belgian Ardennes and who in their skeletons clearly combined human characteristics with others that were much more simian. All things considered, no one knew quite what to do with these creatures. We had to wait until 1908 before the complete skeleton of the Neanderthal man was discovered in France by three young abbés who were passionately interested in anthropology; it was immediately described by one of the greatest of French paleontologists, Marcellin Boule. Then the true nature of the Neanderthal man was recognized.

*

Meanwhile, a sensational discovery of prehistoric man had thrown the world of learning into confusion, and had probably for the first time stirred up the journalists and aroused public feeling simultaneously, for it posed many more problems than it solved.

This discovery had its origin in Holland in 1858, when there came into the world a child of destiny who answered to the otherwise quite French name of Eugène Dubois. Here was a young man who, after a brilliant student career, found himself at the age of 28 years, a lecturer in anatomy at the University of Amsterdam, giving promise of a very brilliant career in the teaching profession. But a secret demon had hold of him: he was passionately interested in prehistoric man and he was persuaded that the discovery of our ideal ancestor, the man-ape, should fall to him. One can imagine that Eugène Dubois argued the matter with himself more or less as follows.

By his studies in medicine and the natural sciences, he was well informed of the discoveries of fossil bones made during recent years. On the other hand, he had been much moved by reading the works of Darwin, and especially those of a German naturalist, Ernst Haeckel. The latter, having become blind when he was scarcely more than 30 years old, had devoted himself—and for very good reason—to theoretical studies of the origin and evolu-

tion of living creatures. Now Haeckel, immediately converted to
Darwin's ideas, undertook to set up a genealogical table of living
creatures. Between 1870 and 1880, and almost one after the other,
he published three volumes entitled *General Morphology of Organisms, History of Creation* and *Anthropogeny or the History of
Human Evolution*. Thoroughly exploiting Darwin's ideas on evolution and its working, he demonstrated that all living creatures had
one common ancestor; and that there is then a progression from
the simple to the complex organism, the whole of Haeckel's evolutionary plan starting from a microscopic creature which he called
the moneron. This creature was unfortunately hypothetical, just
as were the numerous intermediate animals that Haeckel thought
up in order to link the different zoological groups, sometimes with
some difficulty. If some of the ideas suggested by the German
naturalist were clearly exaggerated, several of them, on the other
hand, found striking confirmation in later discoveries. Such is the
case so far as concerns the origins of humanity.

When, in fact, in order to bring his genealogical tree of living
creatures to completion, Haeckel sent down the roots of the human branch into the ape group, he was led to suppose the existence
of a creature intermediate between the anthropoid apes and man,
a creature to which he had assigned in advance the evocative name
of *Pithecanthropus*, that is to say, ape-man. Now Dubois, having
read and re-read Haeckel and Darwin, and having studied the
discoveries from Neanderthal, Gibraltar and Spy, and after having grasped the importance of the work of Boucher de Perthes
and Lartet, decided that this ape-man was his to discover. Where
on the surface of the earth was he to find him? For Dubois the
answer was simple: the large anthropoid apes were now localized
in two parts of the globe, the orang-utans in the Dutch East
Indies, and the gorillas and chimpanzees in Central and East
Africa. As the Dutch East Indies were by reason of his nationality
more accessible to him than Africa, it was there that he decided to
look for his ape-man. But to make such a search he unfortunately
needed money; so Dubois tried to obtain for himself some job of
exploration. Nevertheless, this little faculty assistant, who both-
ered the professors in their laboratories and disturbed the administrative peace of the civil servants, was regarded by everyone as
a young fanatic. Moreover, his desperate eagerness to discover
what the majority of men regarded as a myth was, in the end,

rather irritating and a little odd. Fortunately for science, this young man was obstinate. Seeing that his teachers had abandoned him, and although his colleagues and friends almost regarded him as mad when they saw him ready to sacrifice a brilliant future, he gave up an official job that allowed him to do some excavating in peace, and decided to set out for the Dutch East Indies at any cost. He was a doctor; it was by gambling with this professional qualification that he succeeded in reaching the lost paradise of the man-apes.

In December 1887, the military doctor Eugène Dubois disembarked at Sumatra to take up his post at the hospital at Padang. Unfortunately he was too busy with his invalids to undertake any diggings before the middle of 1888. On that occasion he was able to go to Java to explore some caves, but without any success. Dubois was not discouraged. At the end of that year he learned that a skull, obviously very old, had just been discovered on the island of Java, at Wadjak. He went there as soon as he could, was able to get possession of the skull and himself found a second in the same bed. Curiously, however, he kept this discovery a close secret for about 30 years and only in 1921 disclosed the existence of the two skulls, which were moreover the skulls of modern men without much paleontological importance.

But Dubois was thenceforth convinced that it was in this region, in Java, more or less in the centre of the island that he would find the man-ape. In November 1890 a fragment of a human lower jaw, with one tooth still in place, was discovered at Kedoeng Broboes. Dubois felt that the goal was near. He hurried to the district and started systematic diggings.

This region is situated in the eastern half of the island, where a series of volcanoes rises, some of the craters still being active: Witis, Merapi, Lawu-Kukusan, and others. Rising on the slopes of the latter and flowing around it from south to north, then twisting around it on the west, to run at last into the Pacific Ocean, a river called the Solo carves its bed through the ash hurled from the crater in earlier times. And it was while digging in the clay and volcanic debris which flank the river north of Lawu-Kukusan, not far from the village of Trinil, that Dubois, in September 1891, brought to light the third upper right molar of an ape-man. Some weeks later, at the beginning of December, three yards from the spot where he had found the tooth, he discovered

Tertiary   Lavas   Ash and tufas

FIG. 10. The island of Java and the site of the *Pithecanthropus* discoveries.

the top of the cranium of what was thereafter considered to be *Pithecanthropus*, as promised by Haeckel. He had longer to wait before he discovered, in August 1892, a femur that was buried not far away. But the site where he had found *Pithecanthropus* had meanwhile provided Dubois with a very great number of animal bones, the remains of elephants, rhinoceroses, hippopotamuses, tapirs, antelopes, and dog-faced monkeys.

Dubois devoted himself to a geological study of the stratum in order to determine its relative age. Unfortunately, these animals had been drowned; their dead bodies had then been carried along by the river and for some reason had been deposited on its banks at a certain spot. The same applies evidently to specimens of *Pithecanthropus*, a fact which at the end of the last century helped to lessen its value. But in order to fix one's ideas, it may be said that the man-ape of Java lived some hundreds of thousands of years ago—let us say between 300,000 and 100,000 years before our era. Nevertheless, Dubois quickly returned to Europe and showed his precious discovery to the Third International Congress of Zoology, which was held at Leyden, in Holland, in 1895. There the discussions between specialists were truly impassioned. Even the general public was aroused and the cranial dome, the two teeth and the femur of *Pithecanthropus* made a small tour of Europe which led from Holland to Paris, Liège, London, Dublin, Berlin and finally to Jena.

The great enigma of *Pithecanthropus* is that it paradoxically combines the characteristics of ape and man. Of the ape it has the flat cranium, the bony excrescence above the orbits (the brow ridge), and that other bony excrescence above the nape (the occipital ridge); it also has ape-like teeth. On the other hand, the femur shows very little difference from the femur of modern man. This was one of the main subjects of discussion between zoologists and paleontologists, for many refused to admit that so human a femur could have been associated with so simian a cranium. Besides, it was also questioned whether the teeth had belonged to the same individual as the cranium. Others, taking the stand which was that of certain detractors of the Neanderthal man, sought to regard *Pithecanthropus* as a diseased or abnormal creature. Finally, the age of the fossil was also disputed, arguing from the fact that Dubois was not a professional geologist but an anatomist and that he certainly could have made mistakes in his study of the stratum.

It must be recognized, moreover, that this study was quite difficult, since *Pithecanthropus*, like the surrounding animals, had been
drowned and carried a longish way from its original habitat before
it was cast up and buried in the alluvial deposits of the bank.
However, from the studies of later geologists, conducted by experts of unquestionable repute, we can fix the age of *Pithecanthropus* between 100,000 and 300,000 years.

For many scientists since that time, at the beginning of this
century, an intermediate creature has been sandwiched between
apes and men: the man-ape of Java, Dubois' *Pithecanthropus*,
which should be considered more or less as one of our direct ancestors. Other scientists, and especially the great majority of the
French, under the guidance of Boule, looked on it only as a giant
gibbon. These scientists, certainly, did not deny the existence of
fossil man, but they showed very great caution. They laid especial
emphasis on the discoveries made at Neanderthal and Spy and
hoped to find an acceptable intermediate creature in the Neanderthal man. In 1908, this man, or rather his skeleton, in a state of
admirable preservation, was offered them on a platter.

*

That summer, three young abbés, Amédée and Jean Bouyssonie
and Louis Bardon, were spending their holidays in Corrèze, south-
east of Brive, at a little town called La Chapelle-aux-Saints, situated
almost on the boundary of the department of Lot. Exploring a
little cave at the outskirts of the village, they began by throwing
out some loose soil, then some not very thick clayey sand, and
uncovered a bed of compressed earth that was much harder,
about 12 to 15 inches thick, where they found numerous stone
implements and animal bones. In this cave had lived—at least
provided they had not been brought there by carnivorous beasts
—bison, reindeer, woolly rhinoceroses, marmots and cave hyenas,
as evidenced by the numerous bones. Finally, on August 3rd, 1908,
three yards from the entrance to the cave the three abbés uncovered a human skeleton which they hurriedly released and sent to
Marcellin Boule at the National Museum of Natural History in
Paris. Boule soon found himself in possession of the almost complete head, also of "twenty-one vertebrae or fragments of vertebrae,
a score of ribs or fragments of ribs, a clavicle, the two almost

complete humeri, the two incomplete radii, the two ulnas, some bones of the hand, two pieces of the iliac bones, two incomplete femora, two patellas, parts of the two tibiae, an astragalus, a calcaneum, the five right metatarsals, two pieces of left metatarsals, and a phalanx," as he himself recorded. The reconstituted skeleton can be seen to-day at the Musée de l'Homme in Paris. At the time it was a very important event, for it was only the second time that an almost complete skeleton of prehistoric man had been found, 30 years after Rivière's discovery at Menton, which will shortly be described, since this was in any case a "very modern" fossil.

After several years' work, Marcellin Boule was able to present a remarkable reconstruction of the Neanderthal man. He had a large head on a small body and was only between 5 feet 1 inch and 5 feet 3 inches tall; although he stood upright, he walked with stoop, head thrust forwards and knees bent. The face was very massive in relation to the volume of the cranium, and had a muzzle-like projection. The cranium was flat (known as platycephalic), with a receding forehead; in front, like *Pithecanthropus*, although less pronounced, was a bony ridge above the orbits, and an occipital ridge at the back. When viewed from above, this skull reveals a very distinct narrowing behind the brow ridge. The brain reached the size of that in modern man, being around 1,540 c.c.; in the case of the specimen from La Chapelle-aux-Saints, which was 1,600 c.c., it was even abnormally developed. On the other hand, so far as can be judged by the plaster casts, the structure of the brain seems to have been much more simple than that of modern man; especially noticeable is the great development of the zones called visual, at the expense of the frontal parts of the brain, known as the frontal lobes. This feature brings the Neanderthal man closer to the animals, especially the higher apes. In fact, zoology and paleontology teach us that the vertebrates, in proportion as their cerebral faculties develop, reveal correlatively a tendency to the regression of the olfactory and visual areas and to the enlargement of the volume of the frontal lobes. The work carried out by the physiologists for several decades has assigned to these frontal lobes the power of association, that is, the seat of the intelligence is almost regarded as being in this area. The question, in its physiological aspect, is rather beyond the scope of this work, and it is sufficient, in order to understand the problem of

human fossils, to connect the development of the frontal lobes
with the manifestation of a higher cerebral activity.

Finally, Boule tried to go a little further in the restoration of the
Neanderthal man. We shall let him speak for
himself; although his studies went on for another 40 years and he died in 1942 at the age
of 80, this rough and tenacious Auvergnat became one of the world's leading paleontologists; he remains and will remain the great
specialist on this fossil man:

"The only attempt in which I thought it
possible to indulge is as follows. To a young
sculptor named Joanny-Durand, who was an
enthusiastic student of anatomy, I gave a cast
of the skull of the Man of La Chapelle-aux-
Saints. I asked him to model the principal
muscles in plasticine and to superimpose
them, one by one, on this plaster cast, pro-
ceeding from the deep layers to the superficial layers and carefully adjusting their in-
sertion. Their strength permits us to appreciate to some extent the power of the
relative muscles. Far from forcing his work
in a simian, animal direction, which would
have been easy, the artist remained as far as
possible in a human sentiment. Apart from
the shape of the ears and the tip of the
nose, for which we had no data, our reconstruction would not diverge far from the
true appearance of the skinless head of our
fossil man. I leave to readers the task of
studying this physiognomy, of finding there
the morphology of the skull, of comparing
it with the faces of real man and of asking
themselves what any cutaneous and hairy
covering would add to the expression of this physiognomy, so
well as the more or less dramatic play of the muscles presented
here in a state of rest." (See halftone illustration.)

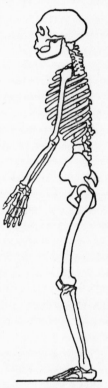

FIG. 11. The skele-
ton of the Nean-
derthal man as re-
constructed by
Boule after the
specimen from La
Chapelle-aux-
Saints.

*

At the beginning of this century a German doctor practising in

China, Dr. K. A. Haberer, was occupying his leisure in making a very curious collection, one that could only be made successfully in China. He was collecting fossil teeth. It so happens that Chinese healers used very curious medicines, ranging from snake skins to the placentas of dogs and including fragments of bone or teeth which in the main were attributed to fabulous dragons. These bones and teeth were in fact fossil bones and teeth from animals that have long since disappeared from Chinese soil. All these medicaments were sold in the apothecaries' booths, which might be called dispensaries. It was while haunting these dispensaries, as others haunt antique shops, that Haberer succeeded in getting together a very fine collection of fossil teeth of great scientific value, which he forwarded to Max Schlosser, the professor of paleontology at the University of Munich. After detailed examination, Schlosser published his results in 1903 and described, in particular, a third upper left molar of almost human appearance. He drew attention at the same time to the apparent antiquity of this tooth, as deduced from its external aspect (in fact there is, to the eyes of a specialist, a clear difference between fossilized bones that are several tens of thousands of years old, and more recent bones only some tens of centuries old). This is probably the first scientific mention of the Pekin man, but, less daring than was Black, the Canadian, 25 years later, Schlosser did not dare to construct a history of prehistoric man in China on the basis of a single tooth.

The discovery and study of the Pekin man, begun by a German and corroborated by a Canadian, have certainly a very cosmopolitan look, for it was a Swede who provided their first foundations, which were brought to completion by the combined researches of a Frenchman, a Chinese and an American. In 1916, Dr. Andersson arrived from Sweden as an adviser to the Chinese geological service which had just been created. As a part of his job he inspected mines and quarries, and during these visits collected bones and teeth which he sent to the University of Uppsala. In 1920 he was inspecting the chalk quarries of Choukoutien, about 25 miles south-west of Pekin; these quarries were, in fact, caves dug into limestone cliffs, rather like the caves and pits that in France are hollowed out by the waters that infiltrate the limestone plateaus of the Causses. During this inspection, Andersson noticed that certain fissures were filled with red earth of a very

special appearance, a sort of fine and very light sand; taking a
closer look he gathered some fragments of fossil animal bones
and, with an instinct that can only be praised in retrospect, decided
that there were doubtless some interesting paleontological discoveries to be made at this spot.

Andersson's reasoning can be summarized in the following way.
These caves and fissures in the limestone hills of Choukoutien had
at one time been empty; something like a million years ago the
limestone hills were raised above the vast plain of Hopei, the
climate was cold, the glaciers that come down from the north
halted not far away, and the violent winds that blew along the
surface of these glaciers gradually filled the pockets in the limestone with the red loess that now completely blocked them. Thus
it was not impossible that some fossils of apes could be found
there that might throw new light on the evolution of this group
and, perhaps, on the origins of man. In any case, since there were
fossils in the limestone fissures, it would not be uninteresting to
study them.

With these convincing arguments, Andersson persuaded Ivar
Kreuger, a patron of arts and sciences in Stockholm, who had an
enthusiasm for things of the past, to subsidize a campaign of
excavations and to send him an assistant in the person of Dr.
Zdansky. Having arrived on the spot, the latter quite quickly
discovered, among all the fossil bones he dug out at Choukoutien,
two teeth of very human appearance. Unfortunately, he hardly
knew what to make of them, especially as these sites at Choukoutien, being considered very old (at least a million years),
the presence there of human or prehuman fossils seemed inconceivable.

Fortunately, in 1925 Canada entered the scene: Dr. Davidson
Black, at his own request, was appointed Professor of Anatomy
at the medical college that had just been founded at Pekin. He was
very keenly interested in prehistoric man: he had a very close
knowledge of all that related to the circumstances of their discovery, and to their anatomical structure, and he had more especially worked on the Piltdown man. It was even with the secret
hope of making a resounding discovery there that he had taken this
post in China. When Andersson and Zdansky showed him the teeth
discovered at Choukoutien, he asked for funds from the Rockefeller Foundation in order to undertake systematic excavations

and, on October 26th, 1927, one of his assistants, Dr. Bohlin, discovered a splendid human molar intact. For a month Black turned it over and over, thinking about it continuously and studying it in its smallest details. On December 2nd of the same year he presented to the Geological Society of China a report on *Sinanthropus pekinensis*, that is to say, the Chinese man discovered at Pekin, a very ancient kind of man who had lived in China more than 100,000 years ago. The matter was the more serious and the stand taken by Black the more sensational as, solely on the basis of a single molar, he predicated the existence at a very distant epoch of a prehistoric man much closer to modern man than to the great apes. Now it was Black who, alone against everyone, was right.

Between 1928 and 1932, thanks to 20,000 dollars granted every year by the Rockefeller Foundation, the discoveries multiplied. A hundred workers, toiling in the excavations, in three years shifted 12,000 cubic metres of earth and the superintendents of the excavations brought to Pekin close on 2,000 cases of fossils. At this moment a young Chinese paleontologist, Dr. Pei, Black's assistant, and Father Teilhard de Chardin, a Frenchman, entered the scene. The latter, by a curious irony of fate, had been sent to China— not to say exiled—because he began to hold what were, to the orthodox Catholic view of the time, rather daring ideas about the origin of man; in consequence of which he was to play an extremely important part in the finest discovery of a man-ape that had ever taken place. During the summer of 1928, Pei discovered a fragment of cranium, a lower jaw-bone and some teeth. In 1929, while digging out some caves at Choukoutien, he came upon the top of a skull which strongly resembled that of *Pithecanthropus* and, in 1930, a second skull. During this time, Father Teilhard de Chardin and Young, the American, studied the bed from the viewpoint of the fossils it contained and the succession of the strata—that is, they determined the age of the sites and therefore of the bones that were contained there, as well as of the fauna in the midst of which *Sinanthropus* lived.

When Black died in 1934 he had had the pleasure of seeing his ideas accepted: the conclusions he had drawn from the study of a single molar were confirmed and it could be stated that a man-ape lived in China more than a hundred thousand years ago.

The excavations and anthropological studies were not halted

by Black's death. The American, Weidenreich, who succeeded
him, was one of the most eminent of contemporary paleontologists.
Teeth, pieces of cranium, and fragments of long bones were extracted every year in quite large numbers. It would be wearisome
to record all the discoveries in their chronological order. On the
eve of the second world war, the Pekin man was the best known
of all fossil men: we have the remains of 38 different individuals,
15 of them being children. War was not to bring luck to *Sinanthropus*. Soon China was invaded by the Japanese. All the bones
were taken into the American medical college at Pekin, where
they filled no less than 63 cases, watched over by Father Teilhard
de Chardin, who had to remain a prisoner of the Japanese for
five years. But after 1945 it was absolutely impossible to lay hands
on a single one of these cases. From the enquiry that was con-

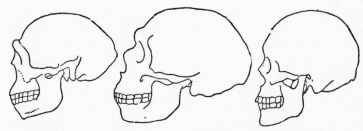

FIG. 12. Comparison of the skulls of *Sinanthropus* (*left*),
Neanderthal man (*centre*), and modern man (*right*).

ducted following their disappearance, there was reason to believe
that the Japanese, when about to evacuate China, had wished to
take the Pekin man to Tokyo, but that the ship that was carrying the cases was wrecked in the China Sea, probably torpedoed
by an American submarine. So that, like his cousin *Pithecanthropus*, *Sinanthropus* ended in a watery grave. This accident,
however, was no serious inconvenience, since, each time a piece
of bone was extracted from the Choukoutien quarries, a cast
had been made at once, and these casts were long since in a safe
place.

So this *Sinanthropus* was a man-ape, whose anatomical description is very like that of the man-ape of Java. In actual fact he was
a *Pithecanthropus* and in all justice he ought to have borne the
name *Pithecanthropus pekinensis*, having regard to the rules of
scientific priority, which requires that the first name given to an

animal or a plant should be retained in the interests of clarity. Just like *Pithecanthropus, Sinanthropus* had a low forehead, a flat cranium, a ridge of bone above the orbits and an occipital ridge at the nape; his face projected, his teeth were intermediate between those of an anthropoid and those of modern man; his long bones, so far as we know them, were very like those of modern man and quite removed from the long bones of the anthropoid apes.

Thus, 100,000 years ago there lived in South-west Asia man-apes whose anatomical features were clearly intermediate between those of modern men and those of real anthropoids. Their existence was further confirmed by the discovery, in 1936, 1937 and 1939 of further remains of *Pithecanthropus* in the island of Java, at Sangiran, some 40 miles west of Trinil, the locality where Dubois had discovered his first *Pithecanthropus*.

Finally, we cannot leave the Far East without speaking of the giants that lived in China and Java something like 100,000 to 200,000 years ago. Between 1934 and 1939 the Dutch geologist von Koenigswald often made the trip between China and Java. In Java he discovered the specimens of *Pithecanthropus* just mentioned. In China he began, just like Haberer some 50 years earlier, to explore the pharmacies of Hong-Kong to discover the riches of the Chinese pharmacopoeia and, as far as possible, to lay hands on fossil bones used as medicaments. It was thus he received three teeth that were fairly human in their conformation, but of quite unusual size, twice that of real human teeth. The creature that possessed them must have been a gigantic ape or man from 8 to 10 feet tall. Imitating Black, who had created a genus and a new species on the basis of a single tooth, von Koenigswald created *Gigantopithecus*. And in 1941, this time in Java, von Koenigswald discovered in rapid succession two pieces of jaw-bone of very great size, still with a few human teeth. These were the remains of a giant man-ape, *Meganthropus*, who must have been 7 feet 6 inches tall. From these discoveries Weidenrich and von Koenigswald have concluded that in its early days humanity passed through gigantic forms which gradually gave birth to smaller forms.

The English paleontologist, Dr. Broom, energetically maintained the same views and it is even thus that he explains the abnormal size of the human brain. In fact, according to him, the stature of the giant men-apes with large brains progressively diminished

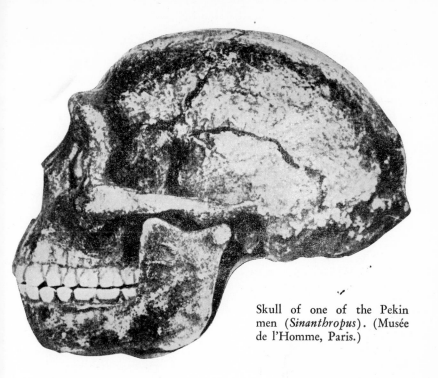

Skull of one of the Pekin men (*Sinanthropus*). (Musée de l'Homme, Paris.)

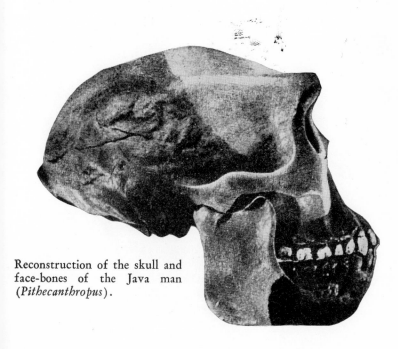

Reconstruction of the skull and face-bones of the Java man (*Pithecanthropus*).

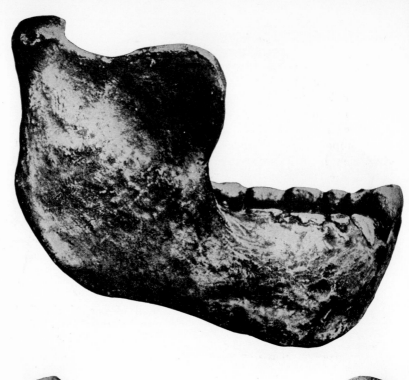

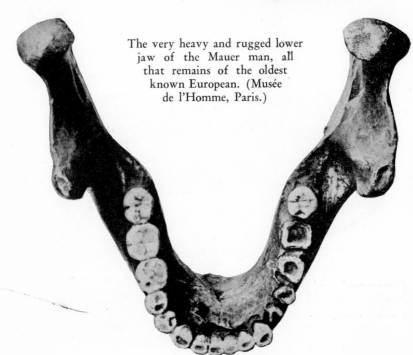

The very heavy and rugged lower jaw of the Mauer man, all that remains of the oldest known European. (Musée de l'Homme, Paris.)

while the brain retained its dimensions, thus becoming enormous in relation to the total structure. Broom emphasized that similar examples are to be found when one studies the dwarf races of certain animals, like horses, dogs, cats and elephants. In reality, this view is very questionable and so far very few paleontologists have supported it. Nothing proves that the ancestors of man have been giants; nothing proves that the origin of the great size of the human brain is to be found in the gigantism of our ancestors.

From all this it remains clear that 100,000 years ago South-east Asia was much populated. Several different species of man-ape have been found there, scarcely differing one from the other except in trifling anatomical features. Certain forms were of very great

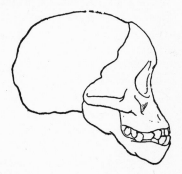

FIG. 13. The skull of *Australopithecus africanus*. It is a chimpanzee-like skull with a jaw, and especially teeth, that are very like those of man.

stature. It will suffice to remember that we are here in the presence of a group in evolution, in the midst of which several attempts in the direction of modern humanity were taking place.

At present it appears that two clearly marked zoological lines made the transition between the anthropoid apes and man: on the one hand, the man-ape of the Dutch East Indies and China, an anatomical mosaic of simian and human characteristics, and on the other, the Neanderthal man, still a little simian and still a little beast-like.

*

It was only in 1924, and between 1936 and 1939, that the first fossil man-apes were found in South Africa, in a particularly interesting form, since they were still closer to the ape than the prehumans of South-east Asia; so much so that we could better speak of them as ape-men than man-apes. Furthermore, they seem to be very old and could very well take their place, at first sight, at the very root of the human branch.

In 1910 the commercial exploitation of the clay quarries in South-west Transvaal began. This clay is deposited along a river, against limestone escarpments. The bulk consists of white clays, but in them the water has carved quite a number of caves where very sandy red clays were subsequently deposited. For ten years the exploitation of these clay beds was uneventful, but in 1920 a workman discovered in one cave a small cranium, which was given to Dr. Haughton of the South African Museum at Capetown. The latter came to the conclusion that this was the cranium of a baboon but a fossil baboon unknown until the present day and, in order to establish its antiquity, he called it *Papio antiquus* (*Papio* being the generic name for a baboon). Between 1920 and 1924 several further baboon skulls were discovered. One of them fell into the hands of Miss Josephine Salmons, at that time assistant to Raymond Dart, the then little-known Professor of Anatomy at the University of Witwatersrand. It happened that Dart, who was very interested in this small skull, knew the manager of the clay quarries personally and he very easily secured a promise that any fossil discoveries would be sent to him. And soon, at the end of the year 1924, a quarryman found the top of a cranium while blowing up a depot at the mine, and, digging a little further, found the facial bones corresponding to it. Dart was very excited when he received these two pieces of bone. He succeeded in cleaning the fossil in less than six weeks, thus creating a new speed record. This was, he declared, a composite creature, half-ape, half-man, but a creature from which, unfortunately, all the hoped-for information could not be extracted, for it was a young creature, a young ape of four or five years or an infant of six years. Dart gave it the name *Australopithecus africanus* (southern ape).

The cranium is remarkable in the sense that it shows practically no brow ridge or occipital ridge of marked degree and that it is not very flat. Further, the foramen magnum through which the spinal cord leaves the brain and enters the vertebral column is placed fairly far forward, as in man, and in any case further forward than in the anthropoid apes, which clearly indicates that *Australopithecus* stood upright. The cranial capacity was 500 c.c.; since this was a child, it can be reckoned that that of an adult would be about 600 c.c., a figure slightly more than that of gorillas and chimpanzees. The face is fairly comparable with that of a young modern child, especially so far as the structure of the eyes and nose are concerned. Finally, the teeth are quite remarkable, for they are absolutely identical with the milk teeth of a child of six years.

The publication of this discovery raised a general outcry and the scientists who consented to give it attention were few. It was generally considered to be an ape, a rather special one certainly, but its paleontological importance was considered to have been greatly exaggerated by Dart. In no event was it admitted that it had any relationship whatever with the human species. Even in England the main discussions did not bear upon the osteology of the fossil, but took a more lofty turn by moving to a linguistic field. In fact, there was little concern to know what sort of ape Dart had discovered and he was even pardoned for having sought to regard it as an ancestor of man, but he was not pardoned for knowing so little of the dead language as to create a Latin name from two Greek roots.

Australopithecus was long forgotten when in 1934 Dr. Robert Broom was appointed to the Pretoria Museum. There he spent eighteen months in local excavations and in studying the fossil reptiles of the region. In May 1936 he too decided to go in search of *Australopithecus* and he did not doubt for a second that he would succeed in discovering an adult. Thus he arrived at Sterkfontein, led there by two of Dart's assistants, who had come to him after he had published his discovery of the remains of a giant baboon.

Sterkfontein is an agricultural station about 30 miles from Johannesburg. Some quite large caves had been discovered on its land in 1895, and two years later Frames reported that the caves were rich in the bones of horses, antelopes, apes, porcupines, rats and bats, which had certainly been dragged there by beasts of prey. These caves quickly became famous in the region and on Sundays numerous tourists came to visit them, guided by Barlow, the foreman of the quarry, to whom science is indebted for the principal discoveries of *Australopithecus*. Barlow claimed to have already seen the workers extract some skulls very like that which Dart had found not far away in 1924. In consequence, Broom did not doubt for a minute that he would find his prey, the adult apeman, at this spot. And, of course, he found it: on August 17th, 1936, Barlow sent Broom the top of a cranium. The following day

Broom was taken to the site of the discovery and himself extracted the base of the cranium and a few pieces of frontal bone. The ape-man he had just discovered was this time an adult. It was a close relative of the *Australopithecus* and was given the name *Plesianthropus transvaalenis*.

At Sterkfontein, in less than a year, Broom was to discover eight skulls of the ape-man, all very like *Australopithecus*; like him, these ape-men stood upright, were of small stature, with teeth very like human teeth in their design; on the other hand, their faces projected somewhat and their skulls were intermediate between those of the anthropoids and those of modern men.

Chance continued to smile upon Broom. On June 8th, 1938, Barlow handed Broom a piece of upper jaw with the first upper molar still in place. Broom was able to acquire it by signing a cheque for two pounds sterling. But on examining this fossil bone more closely, Broom saw that there were two fresh fractures corresponding to the location of two molars; further, the matrix which surrounded the fossil was not identical with that usually found at Sterkfontein. He deduced from this that the bone had been found elsewhere, in a spot eventually fertile in paleontological discoveries, and that, furthermore, someone was in possession of other pieces of this skull, if only the two recently broken teeth. After a lot of coaxing, Barlow eventually admitted the source of this piece of skull: it had been given him by a schoolboy, Gert Terblanche, an occasional guide to the caves on Sundays, when the tourists were too numerous.

Broom eagerly dashed over to the Terblanche farm, which was about two miles from Sterkfontein; unfortunately he only found Gert's mother and sister, who could only tell him the place where the boy had found the piece of skull; but they also gave him a very valuable piece of information, that Gert had taken four teeth from this skull to school with him. Broom went off at once to the site of the discovery, at the top of a hill, where he found some fragments of skull and two teeth. Then he went down again to the school and reached there half an hour after noon, during recess. The headmaster fetched the young Terblanche, who drew from his trouser pockets what Broom described as four of the most sensational teeth in the history of the world. Following which, Broom paid the ransom and gave a little improvised address to the four teachers and 120 children of the school. Then he arranged for Gert to be free for the afternoon to come with him to the top of the hill. There the boy drew from a hole that was carefully filled in the lower jaw-bone of this sensational ape-man, with two teeth in place. Finally, thanks to his tenacity, Broom in three days almost entirely reconstituted the head of the *Paranthropus robustus*. Three months later *Paranthropus* was introduced to the world at large in an article in the *Illustrated London News* of August 20th, 1938, published under a title (which was not Broom's) which suggested that the missing link was missing no longer.

Interrupted by the war, Broom's excavations did not begin

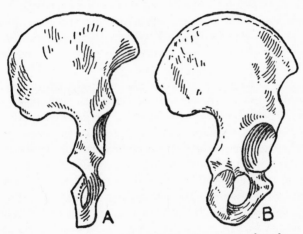

FIG. 14. Comparison of the pelvises of an *Australopithecus* (*left*) and of a South African native (Bushman, *right*). The outlines are roughly alike and clearly indicate that *Australopithecus* had acquired an upright posture.

again until 1947 and in three years they produced some new forms of the *Australopithecus*, differing very little one from another. Once more the scientists were faced with a group in full evolution, this time in South Africa and no longer in Asia, but providing transitional forms between apes and men that are no less interesting; so much so that, following these discoveries, one is much tempted to set up an evolutionary succession still more complete than that pointed out a few pages back: henceforth, between apes and men there are three stages, first the South African *Australopithecus*, then the man-apes of South-east Asia, and finally the Neanderthal men. From one stage to the other the simian characteristics can be seen to diminish progressively, while the human characteristics progressively emerge, in an inconspicuous way at first and then in clearer fashion.

*

But this outline, which will have to undergo quite considerable modification later, is not yet complete. In fact, the line which starts with the South African ape-men does not end bluntly with modern men. Before that, several different races occupied the world scene, but they were anatomically so like ourselves that for a long time they passed unnoticed. The first discovery of modern fossil men dates back to 1823, when Buckland discovered in Wales a headless skeleton, covered with powdered ochre, which he called the Red Lady of Paviland, although in reality it was a male skeleton.

But it was actually in France in 1868 that there were brought to light the first remains of the men of the Reindeer Age. At that time the network of roads was being extended parallel to that of the railways, and at the entrance to the town of Eyzies, in Dordogne, some blocks of limestone were blown up in order to construct the road from Périgueux to Sarlat. After discovering a fairly large number of chipped flints, the workers brought some fossil bones to light. Information was at once sent to Edouard Lartet, who had explored the region five years earlier with Christy, an Englishman. But Lartet was old, and his son Louis was entrusted with the task by the Minister of Education. He soon discovered five almost complete skeletons: an old man, two adult men, a woman and a fetus. In addition, excavating below the spot where the skeletons lay, Louis exposed the remains of hearths—blackened earth and calcined bones—chipped flints, shells and the more or less complete skeletons of animals in fairly large numbers.

The task of studying these skeletons was entrusted to the leading anthropologists of the day: Paul Broca, Pruner-Bey, de Quatrefages and Hamy. The famous Cro-Magnon race—so named because the five skeletons came from the place of that name—had just made its entry into prehistory.

A few years later, at Grimaldi not far from Menton, the prehistorian Rivière profited by the construction of the railway from Marseilles to Genoa by discovering further fossil skeletons of modern men. At this place nine caves open into the red rocks known as the Baoussé Roussé, which overhang the sea. A tunnel was being dug through these caves and it was there that Rivière, on March 26th, 1872, exhumed the Menton man. In 1873 he found three further skeletons and, in the two following years, two skeletons of children. All these were of the same type as those found at Cro-Magnon. Then, in 1901, under the direction and with the financial help of Prince Albert I of Monaco, the skeletons of an old woman and a child were exhumed that were very different from those of Cro-Magnon.

The discoveries multiplied—to such an extent that to-day we have to admit the existence of three different racial types in Western Europe in the Reindeer Age, that strangely recall the three principal types known at the present time: the white, black and yellow races.

The Cro-Magnon type corresponds to the white peoples. These men were very big—their height was on an average between 5 feet 11 inches and 6 feet 1 inch, and they were very robust, so far as can be judged from the size of the marks left by the muscular insertions on the surface of the bones. They were tall-headed and their faces were slightly flattened, with very prominent cheekbones.

On the other hand, the two Grimaldi skeletons correspond more to the black peoples and for this reason they are generally known as the Grimaldi Negroids. They were individuals of small stature, possessing, like modern Negroes, very long forearms and forelegs as compared, respectively, with the upper arms and thighs. In addition, they had prominent lower jaws and very large teeth. These skeletons completely resemble those of modern Bushmen and Hottentots.

Finally, there was a third racial type corresponding to the yellow peoples: the Chancelade type, discovered in 1888 not far from that village in the neighbourhood of Périgueux. Of small stature, too, these men had very well proportioned faces, with prominent cheekbones.

*

This is a very rapid sketch of the principal human paleontological discoveries of the last 100 years. These discoveries have made it possible for us to form a good idea of the different stages bridging the gap between ape and man. In no case, however, do they allow us to write that man is descended from the ape, a con-

venient formula popularized following the work of Darwin but
without real relation to fact; all zoologists and all paleontologists,
beginning with Darwin and Huxley themselves, have condemned
it.

In fact, fine as they are, the exhumations of fossil man just
described are insufficient to explain completely the origins of humanity. On the one hand, these fossils are not the only ones to
have been brought to light several tens of thousands of years after
their burial. On the other hand, one must take into consideration
the intense cerebral activity that distinguishes man, anatomically
and physiologically, whether prehistoric or modern.

This is why, before attempting to set up a genealogical tree for
the human species, that very special field of the mental activities—
industrial, aesthetic and religious—of prehistoric man must be
explored in order to offer a synthesis of any value.

CHAPTER III

Prehistoric Art and Life

A LITTLE Spanish girl named Maria was playing one day in a cave. Not far away, her father, Don Marcellino de Santuola, an archaeologist from Santander, was turning over the earth floor in search of chipped flints. Suddenly raising her eyes, little Maria caught sight of a splendid coloured picture on the ceiling of the cave. *"Toros! Toros!"* she cried; and her father, roused by her cry, was able after a fashion, by the light of some candles, to gaze in amazement upon a parade of red and black bison covering the whole roof of the cavern. This was how, in 1873, the rupestrian form of prehistoric art was discovered.

The incident occurred in the Altamira cave, north-west of the

Fig. 15. The roof-painting in the Altamira cave.

little town of Torrelavega, about twenty miles from Santander, in the mountain chain of moderate height known as the Cantabrian Mountains, that runs from east to west parallel to the northern Atlantic coast. This cavern had been accidentally discovered by a local hunter in 1863, and at intervals, when he had time to spare, Don Santuola came to explore it. Unfortunately, this splendid discovery of prehistoric paintings was repudiated by all the experts, apart from the Spaniard Vilanova and the Frenchman Piette,

and was quickly forgotten. However, one good argument favoured their antiquity. With their humped backs, their large,
wide and deep chests, and their great forward-curving horns,
there was no doubt that the painted animals were bison and everyone knows that bison disappeared from Europe several thousands
of years ago. It was therefore impossible to conceive of fraud, the
more so as over the colours lay a slight calcareous deposit. For a
few, therefore, the Altamira cave contained masterpieces painted
by our very distant ancestors. But for the immense majority of
prehistorians the Altamira cave did not exist.

However, at the beginning of the year 1895, in the little hamlet
of La Mouthe, in the commune of Eyzies in Dordogne, rather
more than a mile south of La Vézère, a farmer named Lapeyre

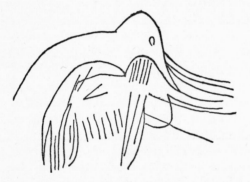

Fig. 16. Mammoth en-
graved on a rock
wall. (Laugerie-
Haute, Dordogne.)

decided to clear out the floor of a small cave which served him
as a cellar. This sort of thing is usual in the district, where the
limestone hills are often sinuously hollowed out into caves of
considerable width and depth; in them provisions, especially wine,
are kept cool. To enlarge such caves the soil that has accumulated
on the floor has to be dug out. But what was the surprise of
M. Lapeyre and his men when, on April 11th, 1895, they uncovered the entrance to a gallery that plunged into the cliff. In
this gallery several village youths, in search of adventure, were
at once swallowed up. By candlelight they crept along for about
a hundred yards and then, while halting for a rest, one of them,
Gaston Berthoumeyrou, suddenly saw some drawings cut into the
rock wall; taking a closer look, he saw that they depicted a kind
of bull—in fact, a bison. The young Berthoumeyrou was not ignorant of the fact that the region had already furnished some

important prehistoric remains, and thanks to him the prehistorian
Emile Rivière was informed at once. From M. Lapeyre, Rivière
secured permission to clear out the gallery, and in the soil that
was excavated he discovered numerous chipped flints. In the end
he was able to reveal, on the walls of the La Mouthe cave, engravings representing several kinds of animals, notably bison, stags,
horses, and a rhinoceros. On September 28th, 1896, a report from
Rivière was presented to the Academy of Sciences. It disclosed the
existence of line engravings done by men of the Reindeer Age;
he had even found a flat and hollowed stone containing traces of
fat, so that he had, in fact, simultaneously discovered the lighting
methods that made it possible for the artists to work more than
100 yards from the entrance to the cavern. However, this report
was not very well received, although the method of excavation,
the discovery of chipped flints, and the portrayal of France long
ago, left no doubt as to the authenticity and antiquity of the
La Mouthe engravings. But they found no more credit with the
scientists than did the paintings at Altamira.

On August 31st, 1896, François Daleau was excavating a cave
where he had made a habit of going in his spare time since 1874.
In this cave, situated at Pair-Non-Pair, not far from Bordeaux,
he had already discovered chipped stone implements comparable
with those found in the Dordogne region and in the Pyrenees;
these simply gave evidence that the Bordeaux region had also
been occupied by prehistoric men. Daleau had long ago observed
some drawings on the rock wall, but he had paid no further
attention to them. But the discoveries at La Mouthe had put him
on the alert, and on August 31st he thought he clearly saw the
engraved outline of a horse. As soon as he could, he returned to
his cave and began to wash all the walls carefully with a vine
spray. In one month he had been able to identify about ten animal
figures which he then made known to the scientific world. Like
de Santuola and Rivière, Daleau received more sceptical laughter
than encouragement.

In the end it was the schoolmaster of Eyzies, Denis Peyrony,
aided by the Abbé Breuil and a local doctor named Capitan, who
at last secured recognition of the true nature of the prehistoric
paintings and engravings. Since the middle of the nineteenth
century important discoveries had been made in the Eyzies region:
in 1863, Lartet and Christy had discovered chipped stones and

engraved bones; in 1868, Louis Lartet had uncovered the Cro-Magnon men; in 1872, a few hundred yards from Eyzies station, the Laugerie-Basse skeleton had been found; in 1888, the Chancelade skeleton had been discovered; and from the first excavations of Lartet and Christy there was no end to the discovery of chipped flints and bone implements, as well as of the remains of animals that have now vanished from Europe, bears, reindeers, mammoths, rhinoceroses, hyenas, and so forth.

On September 15th, 1901, Denis Peyrony was exploring a cave that opened into the side of a hill some 500 yards beyond Eyzies, on the Sarlat road. This was the Font-de-Gaume cave where by candlelight he saw a great number of painted animals. Dr. Capitan, Professor at the School of Anthropology, and Henri Breuil—a young abbé of 24 years, who eventually became Professor of Prehistory in the Collège de France and is to-day one of the unquestioned masters of all that concerns prehistoric art and industry—came at once. This trio of prehistorians had the remarkable luck to carry out a double coup. In fact, half a mile beyond Font-de-Gaume, M. Pomarel, a farmer at Les Combarelles, took it into his head to enlarge a rock shelter that he used as a stable for his draught oxen; he had cleared the entrance of a small gallery and, after creeping with much difficulty for 100 yards, discovered animal engravings on the wall. Still marvelling at the paintings of Font-de-Gaume, which they had scarcely had the time to decipher, Capitan, Breuil and Peyrony looked with wonder on the engravings at Les Combarelles.

Once more the antiquity of these paintings and engravings was duly proved, not only by the light calcareous deposit, transparent or translucent, which covered them, but also by the chipped flint implements in the sand and clay that partly filled the galleries of these decorated caverns. The story of Altamira, La Mouthe and Pair-Non-Pair was repeated. But this time, when the discoveries made in the cave had been concisely presented in August 1902 to the Congress of the French Association for the Advancement of Science, both experts and laymen were convinced. The principal participants at the Congress went to verify the existence of the decorated caves *de visu*. Then they all became excited and the most celebrated and influential of them, Emile Cartailhac, was honest enough to write and publish his *Mea culpa d'un sceptique*.

But Cartailhac went further: he summoned the young Abbé

Breuil to his side and made him undergo a sort of test, asking him to decipher and interpret the engravings and paintings of the Marsoulas cave in the Pyrenees. Enthused by the assurance and learning of Henri Breuil, Cartailhac suggested a trip to Altamira and that same evening wrote to Salomon Reinach asking him to procure a subsidy of 500 francs from the Académie des Inscriptions et Belles-Lettres. By return of post, Salomon Reinach advanced the sum from his own pocket and, on October 1st, 1902, after one of those toilsome journeys of which Spanish trains have the secret, Cartailhac and Breuil reached Altamira. Both were amazed; at Font-de-Gaume the paintings were more or less effaced, at Combarelles and at La Mouthe the engravings were mostly confused, indistinct and difficult to decipher; but here, on the contrary, the polychrome bulls and horses gleamed in the light of the candles. But whereas in the Eyzies region Breuil had been able to copy the paintings and engravings by making traces, at Altamira he had to spend three weeks lying on his back for eight hours a day on sacks of bracken in order to take geometrical bearings on the paintings. The task was expensive: Cartailhac and Breuil would soon have been at the end of their resources if the latter had luckily not brought with him 400 francs which he had just received from Emile Rivière for having traced the La Mouthe engravings.

All the boxes containing the reproductions of these prehistoric works had unfortunately to lie dormant for another three years, for the cost of publishing them was too great. In 1905 Prince Albert of Monaco himself gave the necessary funds for the printing of these monographs. This is probably the place to emphasize the immense services rendered to science, and especially to human paleontology, by Prince Albert's activities, which far surpassed enlightened amateurism. To him, for whom nothing that was human was foreign, we owe the Grimaldi discoveries, the publication of important volumes in colour of the engravings and paintings of the principal decorated caves of South-western France and Northern Spain, and, above all, the creation in Paris of the Institute of Human Paleontology, a research organization inaugurated in 1921, of which Marcellin Boule was the director until 1940. Finally, we must not forget that the Prince of Monaco played the role of patron in other fields, interesting himself also in marine biology and founding the principality's famous Oceanographic Museum.

The discoveries of decorated caves in France multiplied from this time on, principally in the Pyrenees and the Dordogne, but also in Spain in the region of the Cantabrian Mountains. Up till now 70 decorated caves that had been inhabited by hunters of the Reindeer Age have been discovered. Twenty-four are known in the Pyrenees, eighteen in Dordogne, seven in Arièg, four in Lot, four in Ardèche, four in Andalusia, two in Charente, two in Hautes-Pyrénées, two in Castille, two in Basses-Pyrénées and one in Hérault, to which must be added two Italian caves. Account must be taken of the factors that limit such discoveries. Like the Lascaux cave in Dordogne, the majority were explored only by chance; in certain regions where caves are very numerous, one is explored rather than another, thus sometimes passing over a decorated cave in order to examine a simple geological curiosity. Finally, certain caves have sheltered paintings that to-day have disappeared, for when the entrance is fairly big, warm air deposits water-vapour on the walls and thus contributes to the rapid destruction of the paintings; this is probably what happened at Font-de-Gaume.

But when a decorated cave is discovered it is still necessary to make certain of its authenticity. This is probably the most imimportant question for the layman, who never fails to be surprised, and often does not hide his scepticism, that it is possible to assure him that this painted bison or that engraved mammoth or this outline of a hand was done 30,000 or 40,000 years ago. However, certain arguments can furnish proof of their incontestable authenticity. When an animal is depicted that has long disappeared from the region—like rhinoceroses, mammoths, bears, reindeer, bison, etc.—one can only be in the presence of old paintings or modern fakes. Now paleontology tells us when these animals vanished and at the same time provides a method of dating. Another proof of authenticity is the frequent necessity of clearing the cave of the soil which either wholly or partly obstructs it, before being able to examine the rupestrian engravings and paintings; when the soil contains chipped flint implements, authenticity is incontestable and it is again possible to date them. Finally, in very many cases, as at Lascaux, the surface of the rock wall is covered with a very light and completely transparent calcareous coating which could only have been deposited there by the geological processes of many centuries.

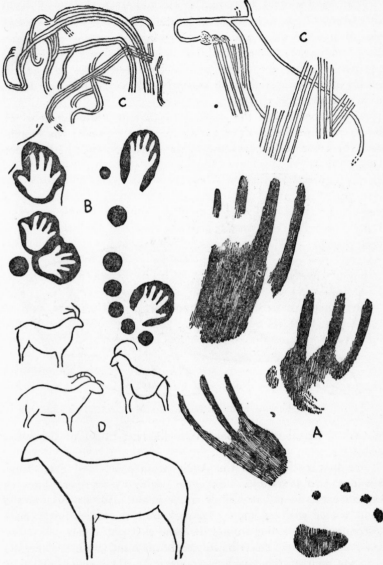

FIG. 17. The evolution of painting methods during the Aurignacian:
(*a*) outlines of hands dipped in colour, from La Baume de Latrone;
(*b*) hands surrounded by colour, from Le Castillo, Spain; (*c*)
animals done by finger-scraping, from La Baume de Latrone;
(*d*) simple line sketches in one colour, from Pair-Non-Pair.

Thus we can not only determine approximately the age of works of rupestrian art but—what is in the end much easier—we can classify the paintings and engravings in relation one to another. From these studies of relative chronology and absolute dating, the experts—notably the Abbé Breuil—have been able to sort the works of art into various schools and establish the principal stages of artistic creation within these schools.

When considering the Franco-Cantabrian area alone, which stretches from the south of the Charentaise region to the North-Atlantic coast of Spain, taking in the Dordogne and the Pyrenees,

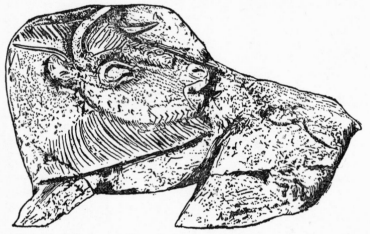

FIG. 18. Polychrome bison in relief. (La Madeleine, Dordogne.)

the Abbé Breuil distinguished two different cycles of decorated caves.

The first cycle covers the Aurignacian epoch and dates from about 40,000 years ago. This cycle begins by representations of human hands in red or yellow, some being made by placing the hand, coated with colour, on the rock wall, the others being made by applying the colour around the hand as it rests against the wall; as a great majority of left hands can be observed, we may conclude that the men of this epoch were already right-handed. The first cycle of decorated caves continues with line drawings done in the clay that covers the cave walls; these formless designs are called "macaronis." Later appeared what the Abbé Glary called finger-scraping engravings: the artist created animal figures by running

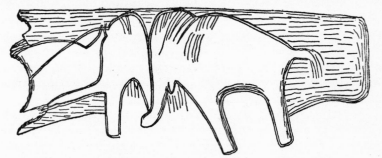

FIG. 19. Mammoths fighting. (Laugerie-Haute, Dordogne.)

FIG. 20. Female reindeer with young. (La Madeleine, Dordogne.)

FIG. 21. Bull. (Teyjat, Dordogne.)

several fingers through the clay, though they were certainly still very sketchy; at other times the figures were covered with colouring matter and a sketchy painting in yellow or red resulted. The proof that fingers were used is provided by the fact that these sketches are always in triple line, corresponding to the use of the first three fingers, by the fact that there is never a really broken line as would have been made by stone implements, and finally by the fact that in the curved parts the lines separate slightly one from another. The caves at La Baume-Latrone, in Gard, and at La Pileta, in Spain in the neighbourhood of Malaga, provide the finest example of these engravings and finger paintings.

Still in the Aurignacian cycle, the next to appear were the line drawings, at first traced with a single fine line, either yellow or

FIG. 22. The famous fighting reindeer of Font-de-Gaume (Dordogne). A specimen of Magdalenian polychrome painting.

red, and later bounded by a line in which thick and thin strokes are visible. At this stage the animals are almost always depicted in twisted perspective, which the Abbé Breuil, creator of the term, defines thus: the animals are represented in profile but the ears, horns, and hoofs are represented full-face or three-quarter face, and sometimes even the internal organs appear as if they were visible through the skin. The first cycle of decorated caves reached its maximum development with the systematic use of colour, first in flat tint, and then in two colours or in polychrome, as for instance those splendid animals at Lascaux and Altamira painted in red ochre, with extremities and muscles emphasized with black.

Besides the twisted perspective, the Aurignacian animal portrayals are characterized by their realism, both intellectual and visual. The finest paintings show animals in action, browsing, running and leaping, no longer motionless, and they are as realistic as photographs.

Besides paintings and engravings, the first men of the Reindeer Age executed some sculptures of very fine appearance, like those discovered at Laussel by Dr. Lalanne. However, during the Aurignacian cycle painting and engraving were always clearly separated, and it was exceptional that an engraving served as a first sketch or as basis for a painting, which is contrary to what happened in the second cycle of cave decoration.

This second cycle, corresponding to the Magdalenian epoch, which is reckoned to date from 25,000 years ago, shows almost the same stages as the Aurignacian cycle. Everything happened as

FIG. 23. The prehistoric "pin-up" discovered by Miss Garrod a few years ago. It is probably the only truly realistic human representation in which body features are not grossly deformed. (Angles-sur-l'Anglin, Vienne.)

if the artistic tradition had been suddenly lost and then, several thousand years later, had been reinvented by the Magdalenians. Thus the paintings of the second cycle of cave decoration begin with line drawings in thick and thin strokes, and end with flat tint and finally polychrome.

We have now only to discuss what techniques were used by the artists of the Reindeer Age to create their paintings and engravings. The pigments were found in certain geological strata: they consisted of iron salts for red and yellow, and of manganese salts for black. These minerals were reduced to powder which could be used in two different ways. Sometimes they were incorporated with semi-solid fatty matter, probably derived from slaughtered beasts, and the pigment was then spread upon the rock walls either with the fingers or with a sort of brush made by fraying a branch at one end (perhaps, as certain primitive tribes still do, by chewing) or properly made of hair or feathers. Sometimes, on the other hand, the powder was blown straight on to the rock wall through a hollowed bone or branch, or directly from the mouth, as is still the practice of certain Australian aborigines: it is the method of the airbrush, and at Lascaux, for example, denser patches corresponding to the centre of the jet can be clearly distinguished.

Because these paintings were very often carried out at the far ends of the caves, the artists had to solve the lighting problem. They used either stones that were hollowed out to form a bowl and contained a little fatty matter with a dry piece of plant matter as a wick (like those found by Rivière in the cave at La Mouthe), or very thin sandstone slabs, one end being covered with fatty matter together with a wick (like those covered with lampblack discovered by the Abbé Breuil in great numbers in the Trois-Frères cave in the Pyrenees), or resin torches. Finally, the high position of some of the pictures suggests the use of accessories to raise the artist above the ground—ladders, ropes or perches.

The engravings were made in the soft clay covering the cave wall with a finger, or with very hard flints capable of cutting relatively fragile limestones.

But the works of art are not limited simply to paintings and engravings. Very fine bas-reliefs have been found as well as clay models, of which the most famous is probably the bison frieze discovered at Tuc d'Andoubert in the Pyrenees. Finally, we must mention the existence of numerous working implements—hunting weapons especially—ornamented with drawings, carvings or engravings. The most famous of these is undoubtedly that discovered by Lartet of a mammoth engraved on a mammoth's tusk. These engravings were very often made on what have been called *bâtons de commandement,* staves of authority. These are fragments of reindeer antler with a hole bored through them, the purpose of which remains a mystery despite the name we have given them: nothing proves that they were emblems of power and they can equally well be regarded as arrow-straighteners, tent-pegs, tool handles, and so forth.

Our final problem is that of the origin and significance of the art. According to the theory put forward by Obermaier, a Swiss who worked with Breuil and Peyrony in the French caves for a

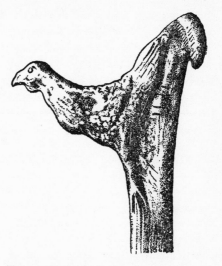

FIG. 25. End of a spear-thrower, decorated with a black-cock. (Le Mas d'Azil, Haute-Garonne.)

FIG. 24. *"Bâton de commandement."* (La Madeleine, Dordogne.)

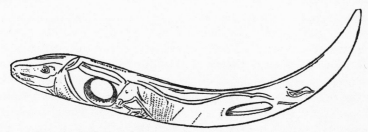

FIG. 26. Engraved *"bâton de commandement."* (La Madeleine, Dordogne.)

very long time, man disputed with the wild beasts—especially cave bears—for possession of the caves that served as his dwelling; on the clay surface of the walls the bears left very distinct claw marks and it was from a desire to imitate these claw marks that man first came to sketch the "macaronis" and later to trace the animal outlines.

This explanation seems a little forced and to-day we can group
the views on the origins and significance of prehistoric art in two
main schools. For some this realistic art was essentially utilitarian,
giving expression to the existence of a magic ritual. In support of
this thesis it is pointed out that the engraved, painted or sculpted
animals are always those which a hunting people would covet
because they provide the materials indispensable to the life of the
human group: food, clothes and weapons. Furthermore, these
animals are often depicted wounded, pierced with arrows or, so
far as we can judge, caught in traps. By representing such scenes

FIG. 27. Man disguised as an animal, with reindeer. (Trois-Frères
cave, Haute-Garonne.)

and by performing certain ritual ceremonies before them, the
sorcerer ensured a successful hunt. Such magical practices still
continue among many primitive peoples. It is one of the features
of primitive mentality to notice that in sunlight the coveted
animal is always accompanied by its shadow and, by representing
this shadow—that is to say by sketching the animal—there is every
chance of catching it. Finally, in support of this theory of a
utilitarian art, it is suggested that as the females are often depicted
pregnant, there is evidence of the existence of certain fertility rites
ensuring the multiplication of the quarry, and therefore being
provisioned at all seasons.

Also, to this idea of fertility rites must be linked the existence of

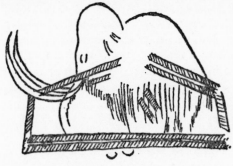

FIG. 28. Trapped mammoth. (Font-de-Gaume, Dordogne.)

FIG. 29. Sorcerer in a boar's mask. (Trois-Frères cave, Haute-Garonne.)

FIG. 30. Stag facing a trap. (Les Combarelles, Dordogne.)

human portrayals, which are fairly rare in the works of art of the Reindeer Age. A certain number of female statuettes are known, each of them being called a *Vénus:* the breasts and genital organs are always strongly emphasized and certain of these statuettes doubtless represent pregnant women. On the other hand, male representations are very rare, if one excepts a few phalluses. There, too, one should see proof of a fecundity cult.

The partisans of utilitarian art make the most of the fact that the paintings and engravings are always situated in very secluded places and that they must often have been done in very difficult conditions. At Les Combarelles, for example, the first engravings appear some 130 yards from the entrance to the cave, and at La Mouthe nearly 100 yards. Thus, in order to execute them, the artist had to isolate himself for many hours at the far end of the cave and other men of the tribe had to be willing to provision

him, which is inconceivable unless he performed a useful function
for the tribe. Further, these engravings and pictures remained
hidden to the people at large and, beyond the sorcerer-artists themselves, would only be known to a few initiates. The sorcerer himself is sometimes represented in the paintings, and the most famous
of these is the one in the Trois-Frères cave, masked and wearing
the skin and antlers of a reindeer.

The supporters of the theory of art for art's sake reply that it is
difficult to understand why prehistoric man should have taken so
much trouble to portray the animals when, for magic ritual purposes, simple hastily-drawn pictures would have sufficed. They also
make the most of the fact that the paintings and engravings do
not necessarily begin very far from the caves' entrance and that
at Font-de-Gaume, for example, to cite only one instance, the
animal representations are close to the entrances. In certain cases
the sculptures are found wholly exposed to the open sky, as at Cap
Blanc.

In fact, as in many things, it seems necessary to adopt a middle
view. Materializing his daily preoccupation with provisioning, but
carried away by his subject, man passed beyond the utilitarian
framework of the first magical representations and, moved by a
feeling for the beautiful, achieved magnificent pictorial or sculp-
tural compositions in which art for art's sake came close to eclipsing
the material interest of the work. In conclusion one cannot do
better than quote the views of the Abbé Breuil, which are full
of common sense:

"There have been frequent discussions with a view to deciding
whether the artists created these works for the love of art, simply
for the satisfaction of having done so, or whether they were engraved or painted with the object of bringing the animals they
hunted to their ends by magical means. There is no contradiction
between these two views, which are not mutually exclusive but,
indeed, complementary. We cannot claim that every line or every
figure had a magical purpose, and in certain cases we can conceive
that to sketch an outline rapidly could for the artist have had no
more importance than to affirm his personality to himself and to
other visitors to these places, if they have preceded them there,
a little like the visitors of to-day who have an urge to scribble
their names. Again, it is clear that there are a number of figures
that require considerable time for their execution, and real skill

FIG. 31. Bouquetin wounded by an arrow. (Niaux, Ariège.)

in design and technique is evidence both that the artist took genuine
aesthetic pleasure in creating his work, and also that the social
environment in which he lived took a large part in the execution
of such works and assured their creator a life free more or less
from daily cares, for his works arose in the satisfaction of needs
considered by his fellows as essential to their existence.

FIG. 32. Lassoed reindeer. (Les Combarelles, Dordogne.)

Fig. 33. Hunting a wild boar. (Agua Amarga, Spain.)

"Nobody disputes that in Egypt art was devoted to the cult of the dead, nor that in the Middle Ages art was almost entirely subservient to the Christian ideal; similarly, in the Reindeer Age our painters and sculptors, no less artists than the Egyptian priests and the image-makers of our cathedrals, found, thanks to beliefs in hunting magic, a magic of reproduction and destruction, the social reason to exercise, develop and teach their art. They were artists and magicians at the same time, painting for the love of art,

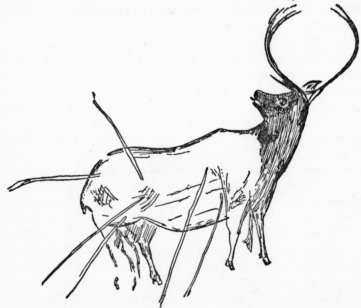

Fig. 34. Stag wounded by a shower of arrows or spears. (Peña de Candamo, Cantabria, Spain.)

but also that the desired game should multiply, that the hunt might be propitious, that maleficent beasts might be destroyed. Art, principally in little developed societies and civilizations, could not persist and grow except by penetrating an occupation judged by them to be essential."

To conclude this survey of the artistic activity of prehistoric man, the existence of music and dancing in the Reindeer Age must be mentioned.

The origins of music and dancing are to be found very deep in the human past, since a certain sense of rhythm can be observed even with some of the great apes, especially the chimpanzees. Both in freedom and captivity the most competent observers, like Carpenter, Koehler and Zuckermann, whose authority is beyond dispute, have often seen chimpanzees perform a childish round while holding hands. Sometimes these rounds are directed by a sort of master of ceremonies, who leads the dance by clapping his hands and striking his feet on the earth. Sometimes, too, the females dress themselves up for these dances with lianas and leaves. Undoubtedly, the men of the Reindeer Age knew about dancing, which, in certain circumstances at least, was accompanied by music. Numerous mural drawings give evidence of this.

Some of the musical instruments used by prehistoric man are known, for they have been found during excavations. The principal ones were pipes cut from bone, flutes that in several paintings and engravings are shown in the hands of the sorcerer, and especially bull-roarers. These instruments were cut from reindeer antlers and a splendid specimen has been found in Dordogne in the La Roche cave. Even to-day some primitive tribes use these bull-roarers by tying them to cords and whirling them above their heads to produce more or less harmonious sounds. Flutes, pipes and bull-roarers are still very often used in our days by some peoples to make the spirit voices heard during magical ceremonies.

Whether this art is in fairly close relation to the physical needs of the individuals or whether it is a purely intellectual manifestation, the study of the origins and significance of art results in raising certain questions concerning the life, both individual and collective, of prehistoric men, especially the men of the Reindeer Age. The natural first question concerns the respective places held by religion and magic.

Religious manifestations are found first of all in the cult of the

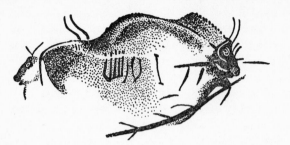

FIG. 35. Wounded bison. (Marsoulas, French Pyrenees.)

dead. Very often, in fact, the skeletons or fragments of skeletons that have been discovered were beyond doubt deliberately buried. Examples are abundant. The Neanderthal man of La Chapelle-aux-Saints (1908) was buried in a geometrically shaped grave; the men discovered in 1909 by Peyrony and Capitan at La Ferrassie in Dordogne were all buried in specially dug graves, surrounded by offerings of food, as evidenced by the presence of pieces of animal skeletons. Again, the skeleton of a Neanderthal man was discovered in the Hissar Mountains of Siberia, north of the town of Baissoum, and around it were disposed in a regular fashion the tops of the skulls of goat-like ruminants, still with

FIG. 36. The "Venus" of Laugerie-Basse. (Dordogne.)

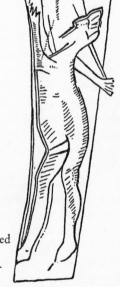

FIG. 37. Small engraved human figure from Laugerie-Basse (Dordogne.)

their horns. At Solutré, in the department of Saône-et-Loire, five skeletons were found buried parallel to one another. Further, like the Red Lady of Paviland and all the Grimaldi skeletons, there was red ochre on numerous skeletons, probably the symbolic representation of blood. At Grimaldi, too, a blue stone was placed upon the middle of the old woman's forehead. In the Trou Violet cave in the Pyrenees pebbles were disposed in such a way as to outline the body of the dead person.

All these facts show beyond dispute that the Neanderthal men and the men of the Reindeer Age had practised a cult of the dead. Moreover, it is not uncommon to find skeletons with their limbs folded back along the body in the position called "fetal," because it recalls the position of the fetus in the womb. Indeed, in order

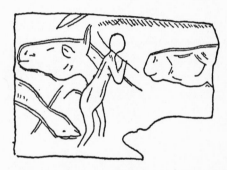

FIG. 38. Small sketch of a human being (leaving for a hunt?). (La Madeleine, Dordogne.)

that they should keep this position for ever, the corpses had had to be placed folded and then tied: perhaps because the fear of death obliged men to bind the bodies and so render them inoffensive, perhaps also because there was a quite simple wish to give parents or friends the ideal position of rest and sleep, and perhaps, finally, because by giving the dead man a fetal posture it was made possible for him to be born again. This last hypothesis brings us to the idea of survival, which was certainly not strange to some peoples of the Upper Paleolithic. It is to this idea of survival that one must attribute the presence of tools, weapons, foodstuffs, decorative objects, and so on around many skeletons. It is probably to this idea, too, that one must relate the symbolic representation of blood in the form of red ochre. But, whatever the hypothesis, it is nevertheless clear that the existence of a funerary cult among prehistoric men is beyond dispute and that it goes back at least some 75,000 years.

The reader will not have failed to notice that during excavations the tops of skulls, intact or broken, are exhumed much more often than any other part of the skeleton. Actually, there are several explanations for this. First, it must be borne in mind that the bones of the cranium are harder and much less fragile than the bones of the face or the long bones of the limbs, also that certain skulls must have been used as domestic implements and that, after having been more or less roughly cut, they served as receptacles. Nor must we exclude the possibility that the intervention of wild beasts or cannibal contemporaries caused the separation of the heads from the rest of the bodies; water action and falls of rock could have had the same result. However, it seems that a skull cult existed during prehistoric times and this was perhaps the first manifestation of the cult of the dead. This skull cult is found in our own day among certain primitive peoples, in Australia, New Guinea, New Zealand, and among the American Indians, etc. Such special attention to the skull of a dead person can have various origins. It is sometimes a simple sign of affection; at other times it is a sign of respect for a particularly remarkable individual, a man noted for his strength and skill, or a woman for her reproductive capacities. On the other hand, the attention paid to the skull by paying homage to the essential part of the individual, arises quite simply from the fear of death; it is a way of appeasing a formidable power. Finally, the skull cult has often as its object the appropriation of the vital force of a parent, or a friend, or an enemy. It happens that, with this end in view, an enlargement of the foramen magnum is made with a view to consuming the brain, and certain tribes justify their practice of head-hunting in this way. Nothing expressly proves that the men of the Reindeer Age were head hunters, but it seems incontestable that, for one reason or another, they practised a skull cult.

From the rites relating to this cult we easily pass to ancestor worship, to the practice of burial with a special orientation of the skeleton, to the disposal around it of accessory articles, to the digging of a tomb, to the placing of slabs above the dead, and so on.

Thus, prehistoric man 30,000 to 40,000 years ago was already *Homo sapiens*, whose cerebral functions, whose moral and religious aspirations scarcely differed, *mutatis mutandis*, from what these have been throughout the historic period and still are to-day.

We are indebted to the anthropologist Vellard for having shown, by a curious personal experience, that humanity thus possesses a common fund of psychic qualities. On an expedition to Paraguay, Vellard had by chance given refuge to a small girl abandoned in their flight by the members of a particularly fierce Indian tribe belonging to the Guayaquil group. Brought up by Vellard's mother, this little girl eventually became Mme. Vellard and is now a distinguished ethnologist, speaking several languages and collaborating very actively and very intelligently in her husband's work. One is not born civilized; one becomes it. And, as soon as he had reached a certain stage of his evolution, prehistoric man had already acquired the essential psychic attributes characteristic of humanity. The rest is a matter of life in society.

*

But primitive art and religion are not sufficient to define the principal aspects of the life of prehistoric man. It was by the chipped stone implements that his existence was discovered and duly proved for the first time. For a thorough study of the life of prehistoric man, his industrial activities must be examined, by passing in review the principal types of implement he made and how they were made.

It is probable, although we cannot produce any formal proof, that the earliest men first used wooden weapons. But these weapons were rarely preserved, for wood is very easily destroyed; fire burns it, shock breaks it and water rots it. However, some years ago, in a swamp in Hanover, a yew spear was discovered between the ribs of a mammoth, and this weapon can be attributed to the Neanderthal man. England, Spain and Germany have also furnished, here and there, fragments of wooden tips and spears.

Nevertheless, it was stone that made it possible for prehistoric man to manufacture his essential tools and weapons. And further, of all the kinds of stones at his disposal he always showed a very decided preference for flint. Flint is in fact one of the hardest of rocks, but one which is nevertheless easy to break because of its foliated crystalline structure. It should further be noted that in their natural state flints often have edges that are fairly sharp, a fact which could have originated the idea of using them as they were or with very slight retouching, thus drawing the attention of early men to the interesting properties of flint as raw material.

But how does one begin to cut a block of flint, to break off thin sheets, or sharpen up the block itself so that its destructive power is increased, however skilfully or unskilfully handled? It was the Frenchman, Léon Coutier, a master stone-cutter, who undertook interesting researches into this subject some years ago. Later he worked at the Musée de l'Homme, when it was founded in 1937. His work has been continued by the Frenchman, Bordes, and the Englishman, Barnes; consequently there is now not much that we do not know about the techniques perfected thousands of years ago for preparing flint weapons and tools.

The prehistoric workmen struck the large flint nodules with a stone or wood striker. The stone strikers, of flint or sandstone, were rather clumsy tools. The hard wood strikers—regularly shaped sticks of oak or box about 8 inches long and a little thicker than a thumb produced thin implements, the finish and delicacy of which it is impossible not to admire. In some cases the cold chisel technique was used, or certainly a technique known as "on the anvil," consisting of throwing the flint violently upon another hard stone—a rock for example, or a large block placed on the ground.

Coutier's researches and those of his pupils were so carefully carried out that, faced with an implement, it is mostly possible to decide which technique was used in its manufacture.

But whichever is used, blows on a large flint nodule progressively detach splinters and the nodule itself grows gradually smaller. The prehistorians call this nodule the "nucleus" and the fragments detached from it the "splinters" if they are short, and "blades" if they are fairly long. Very soon the nucleus, before being shaped, was roughly prepared so that one of its faces was rendered almost flat, the face on which the striking action was exercised and which is known as the "striking plane." The work was thus made easier while increasing the precision of the shaping.

Three principal categories of stone work could thus have existed: the work on the nucleus, in which the splinters were neglected and discarded; the work on the splinters, in which the nuclei were only regarded as raw material without direct utility; finally, the mixed work, using simultaneously the splinters and the nuclei after they had been subjected to adequate retouching. On the other hand, within these categories the shape and variety of the tools makes it possible to distinguish fairly numerous types, the more numerous, moreover, as the years passed, for, after a process of trimming perfected over many years, the investigators could now devote themselves to minute studies, made still easier by the use of physico-chemical techniques recently imported into prehistory. The result is that certain specialists have just made a stand against the breaking up into innumerable varieties of the great manufacturing divisions of the chipped stone age. There is no question of considering this problem here in all its details; it

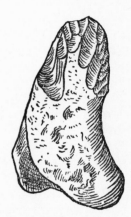

FIG. 39. Types of eolith, flints shaped by natural geological action. (After Rutot.)

will be enough to sketch rapidly the sequence in time of the various types of manufacture.

The first question is that of eoliths. After the discoveries of Boucher de Perthes, everyone set out to find chipped flints and in 1863 the Abbé Bourgeois discovered some in very old strata dating from millions of years ago; from this he at once concluded that man's existence on the earth was very long. Following which, quite naturally, similar discoveries multiplied in France, Belgium, Italy, England, Greece and Portugal. However, these discoveries seemed suspicious; if they were authentic, then one had to admit that man had made his appearance on the earth very long ago, so long ago that at the beginning of the century the anthropologists decided to clear the matter up. First of all there was Marcellin Boule, whose attention was drawn to the work done in a cement factory at Guerville, near Mantes (Seine-et-Oise). There blocks of flint were reduced by crushing-mills to stones of small size; now, after they had been broken, certain pieces of flint were absolutely identical with the so-called implements that were evidence in favour of the great antiquity of man on the earth. Then there was the Abbé Breuil, who collected near Clermont (Oise), in strata that dated from about 50 million years ago, a large batch of these famous flints. The explanation given by the Abbé Breuil was definitely confirmed by the Belgian, Mortelmans, following very

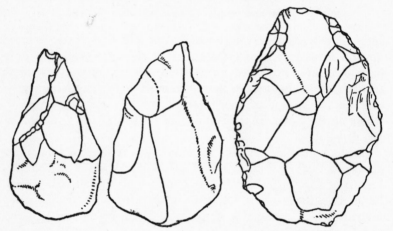

Fig. 40. The roughly cut flint nodules of the Abbevillian.

energetic researches: the flints thus fashioned in the shape of implements had been crushed between blocks of stone rolled along by moving glaciers. Thus, under the influence of natural phenomena—such as rupture by glacier pressure or the effect of heat, or considerable changes of atmospheric temperature—flints have been shaped in such a way as to mimic the tools of prehistoric man. To such flints the name eoliths has been given. They are only freaks of nature which in no way prove the very ancient presence of man on the earth.

About 500,000 years ago chipped stone manufacture really began with the Chellean type (from Chelles, Seine-et-Marne), now very often known as Abbevillian and typified by the use of flint

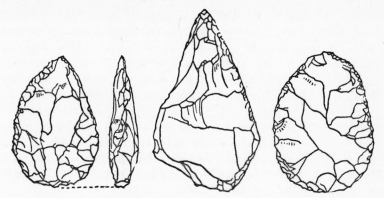

FIG. 41. Faces and profiles of the Acheulian "limandes."

cores roughly shaped as oblate tools, but still fairly little touched up and known as double-faced. Later, the cores were the only parts used, in a two-faced form already less rough and less thick, to which this typical shape has given the familiar name Limandes: this was the Acheulian epoch (from Saint-Acheul, near Amiens, where on the banks of the Somme are the gravel-pits explored by Dr. Rigollot).

At the same time, parallel to these types of worked cores there developed, both in France and England, the working of splinters known as Clactonian (from Clacton-on-Sea), Levalloisian (from Levallois, a Paris suburb) and Tayacian (from Tayac, the commune to which the hamlet of Eyzies in Dordogne belongs). Later, about 100,000 years ago, began the Mousterian (from Le Mouster, in Dordogne); the implements began to be much more varied and

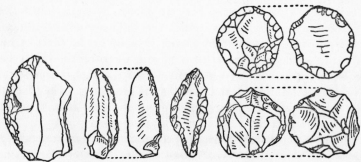

FIG. 42. Implement types of the Mousterian.

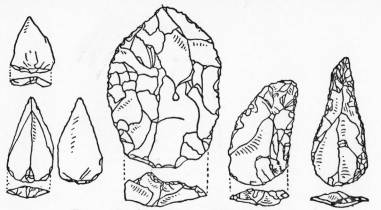

FIG. 43. Implement types of the Levalloisian.

the two main types were a pointed implement the tip of which had been specially fashioned after the splinter had been broken off, and a scraper, one of the edges of which had been made sharp by minute retouching.

Then, in the Upper Paleolithic, the tools became extremely varied: flint scrapers, borers, cutters, blades, chisels and arrowheads. There were also implements made of bone, generally made from reindeer bones: harpoons, daggers, awls, spear-throwers, as well as pins, buttons that resemble our present-day collar-studs, and needles with eyes. The shape of these implements and their finish have made it possible for the experts to distinguish three successive civilizations: the Aurignacian (from Aurignac in Haute-Garonne, explored by Edouard Lartet), the oldest; the Solutrian (from Solutré in Saône-et-Loire), and finally, the Magdalenian (from La Madeleine in Dordogne).

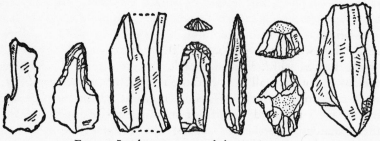

FIG. 44. Implement types of the Aurignacian.

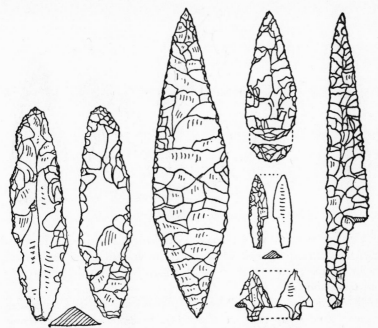

FIG. 45. Implement types of the Solutrian.

The illustrations will show the essential characteristics of these three periods. No one will fail, however, to observe that the names given to these various types of manufacture are almost all taken from French localities, which emphasizes the importance which the science of prehistory, born in France, thanks to Boucher de Perthes, has always received in that country.

*

Such manifestations of human activity—artistic, industrial and religious—imply a rather well-organized collective life and this has prompted several experts to raise the question of the existence of a language permitting communication between members of the same tribe, which takes us back to the problem of the very origin of the spoken word. It is impossible to take account here of the various hypotheses, all very hazardous, which have been put forward to account for the origins of language. All that can be said is that both the mode of life of men in the Reindeer Age and their anatomical structure suggest the existence of a spoken language.

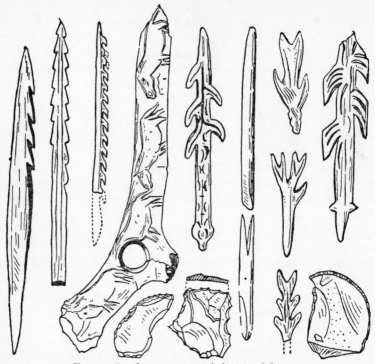

FIG. 46. Implement types of the Magdalenian.

In compensation the tools and weapons of stone and bone, as well as the works of art which have been left us by these men justify us in attempting a reconstitution of what could have been the life of a man in the Reindeer Age, more especially in the Magdalenian.

While the north of Europe, from the North Pole to Holland, was covered by an immense glacier, the region where the Magdalenian man lived (Charentes and Périgord) marked more or less the limit between the tundra, which immediately followed the glacier to the south, and the forested steppe. This transitional zone with a very severe climate in winter, but fairly warm in summer, must have presented fine wooded crests where pine, fir, spruce, larch and birch predominated; elsewhere, where the wind was strong, was the land of scattered willow and dwarf birch copses.

Mosses and lichens were abundant and, on mild days, flowers of striking colour, including saxifrages and gentians, springing up on the plateaus when the last traces of snow, which covered the earth for six months or more, disappeared. In the forests or in the sheltered valleys the herbaceous plants were more numerous and varied and sometimes provided edible roots, leaves and berries.

It was in this landscape that the reindeer developed; it lived in herds which in spring and autumn made great migrations, now moving northwards, now descending southwards, always with a view to finding suitable vegetable sustenance. Very often the cave hyenas, and perhaps other great carnivores too, must have prowled around the herds, watching an opportunity to capture their prey.

It was in this landscape that the mammoth also evolved, as well as the woolly rhinoceros, the polar fox and the arctic hare, without mentioning the smaller rodents and birds. Salmon abounded in the rivers.

But it was the reindeer that was by far the most important of all these animals, the basis of the economic life of man at this epoch. The activity of the Magdalenian tribes was an activity entirely centred upon hunting the reindeer and on the conversion of the products deriving from it. It can be reckoned that 80 per cent of the activities of a Magdalenian, which concerned the material or magical preparation for the hunt, the hunt itself or the exploitation of the prey, were acts which closely or distantly touched upon the reindeer. This might lead us to think that the life of men and women must have been fairly monotonous; now it seems that it was not so, at least as far as the men were concerned.

Certainly, the women would not have taken any great part in the hunting, except perhaps on the occasion of the great collective beats, to frighten the reindeer by cries, wild gestures and showers of stones or sticks. But women had another role in the provisioning; they gathered the wild berries and edible plants, an indispensable contribution to the times when their prey was scarce. It would be absolutely impossible to cite more precisely the names of the plants which might have been the object of systematic collection, for we are ill-informed on the flora of this period. But it is not at all impossible that one day the discovery of the remains of a hearth may bring to light precious botanical evidence.

On the other hand, it may be assumed that the women shared with the men certain responsibilities concerning the preparation and upkeep of the fire, which they then knew how to produce at will, the culinary preparations and finally the manufacture of articles from the skins of reindeer. The principal articles of this kind were clothing, tents, sacks and leather bottles, straps and thongs; the reindeer's sinews, especially the very long and very straight ones from the hoof muscles, were certainly divided into very thin strands and used for sewing. There is good reason to suppose that this sewing was often done with the aid of flat pieces of bone, fairly wide and fairly thick (carpus and tarsus bones, and phalanges), which we call sewing-presses; the bone needle, threaded with a thin piece of tendon, was pushed into the skin with the sewing-press, which thus served like our own thimbles in all major respects. At the end the "thread" was placed on the sewing-press and cut with a blow from a flint. In fact several sewing-presses bear irregular cuts at their extremities which it is logical to interpret as the marks of these flint blows that ended the sewing, while on their sides can be seen little holes that are probably the marks of the needles' heads. Thus a woman's day seems to have been divided mainly between culinary duties and the care of clothing.

As for the men, they had but one occupation: hunting. For this they had first to prepare their weapons; it is probable that each one knew how to make the ordinary weapons, the harpoon, the throwing stick, etc., just as each knew how to make the stone implements necessary to the cutting of reindeer bone. But it is possible there were experts who prepared certain types of weapons for their comrades: in any case there certainly were some individuals in the tribe who were more skilful than others, and from this to specialization is not a long step.

It may also be presumed that the experts got together into workshops whence the weapons and tools were shared out among the neighbouring tribes. Actually we only possess proof of the existence of such workshops for a period more recent than the Magdalenian —for the polished stone age; at that time, moreover, these workshops "exported" their merchandise to distant countries, since we know, for instance, that flints worked in Saône-et-Loire were

transported to Belgium and used there. Similar proofs for the
Magdalenian period are impossible, but one still cannot deny that
there was a certain division of labour.

Furthermore, this division of labour was to be found in other
spheres. There were sorcerers, experts in magic, who were also
talented artists, whose role was to accomplish or direct those acts
the purpose of which was to facilitate hunting and make it fruitful, such as incantations, dances, animal sacrifices and perhaps
human sacrifices too. It is generally reckoned that these artists,
who had to spend long hours in the deepest and often the most
uncomfortable recesses of the caves, more than 100 and even 300
yards from the entrance, were excused from hunting and provided
for by their companions. Moreover, in the primitive minds of
these men, to portray a beast pierced by an arrow or a harpoon was
quite as effective a way of participating in the hunt as to pierce
the animal in reality.

Flat pieces of bone or stone are fairly frequently found, covered
with what at first look like quite meaningless marks in which,
however, one can with great patience distinguish sketches of
animals or hunting scenes. The sorcerer-artists practised before
they went to work properly on the engravings and rupestrian
paintings. Some investigators have concluded—it seems to me a
little hastily—that these were the rough "sketch-books" of ado-
lescents following an apprenticeship as sorcerer-artists.

At least one has to admit the existence of a class specializing in
magic ritual, with all the consequences entailed. Then there were
the "active" hunters, who were numerically the largest part of the
tribe. As regards the business of hunting itself, just as in the
cutting of bone and stone, there were the skilful and the unskilful,
and this leads us to think that during large collective hunts some
were confined to the role of beaters, while the most skilful acted
as marksmen. The great collective hunts, and the most profitable
ones, had to be as frequent as the season and supply of prey
permitted: in the spring and autumn came the great reindeer
migrations, and during the summer the hunters turned their attention to straying herds of bison or horses.

It is thought that the collective hunts consisted in lying in wait
for the herds at the river crossings and turning them from their
course towards the deepest places, where the marksmen waited
to kill them, either at the moment of entering the water or in the

water itself, from the opposite bank or from small boats. Naturally, these large hunts were preceded by magical ceremonies.

When the hunt was over there followed the division of the spoil, which continued during the days that followed in the exploitation of the remains: the skins and the tendons had to be cut up and possibly tanned. It is a fairly simple operation, known to numerous primitive peoples to-day, especially in this particular case as reindeer skins are among the easiest to tan.

Whenever possible, individual hunting and salmon-fishing with harpoons were pursued simultaneously with the collective hunts. In individual hunting or when hunting in small groups, either traps were used (pits, or traps which fell on the animal when it touched the bait) or the creature was tracked sometimes for several days. Mammoths, bears, polar hares and others, were killed in this way.

Although it is quite difficult to reconstruct a Magdalenian's day, it was naturally the need to procure food and everyday objects which filled his time; and although this end could only be reached by following the hunt, there were many acts, material or cultural, to be performed in order to succeed; these must have varied in large measure the life of these Magdalenians which, with all due allowance, must have been less stereotyped than that of many of our contemporaries.

*

A study of the life and art of the Reindeer Age would not be complete without taking account of the osteological evidence concerning the health and disease of prehistoric man. For not only was prehistoric man very often sick, but he knew nothing whatever of any of his diseases. Fortunately modern medicine has filled this lacuna and the work of Dr. Paales is our authority in this new science known as paleopathology.

Undoubtedly, the best known procedure of prehistoric medicine was the operation of trepanning. On certain skulls almost circular holes are to be found, some of which were made after death with chipped stones, while others had been carried out on the living, as proved by the bony proliferation at the edges of the wound which show that healing occurred after operation. It could not be a question of trepanning with a view to operating on the brain, and these holes have been interpreted as designed to allow an "evil spirit" to escape, this evil spirit naturally having its seat in the head, the essential vital organ. This is the opinion held by Professor Pittard of Geneva, as well as other experts. More recently a French military doctor from Marseilles has opposed this theory; he had observed that, of the bony lesions resulting from syphilis, those affecting the cranium are very frequent among certain races —that examination of the skulls of Senegalese soldiers who have died from this disease has revealed holes partly healed at the edges, in every way comparable with the lesions on the prehistoric skulls. The two theories are not incompatible and the argument of syphilitic lesions is not in the end more convincing than that of ritual or magical mutilations, for one can quite well object that

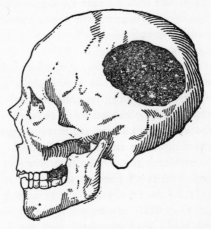

FIG. 47. Specimen of a skull that very probably was deliberately trepanned.

these mutilations are current practice among certain primitive peoples, and have a curative aim.

Further, it has still to be proved that syphilis existed in prehistoric times, and it is in this way that the opinion of the expert from Marseilles is double-edged. For his observations can be used to demonstrate that syphilis is as old as the world, in order thereafter to state that, syphilis being associated with man since his appearance on the earth, it was to this disease that we can attribute what appeared to have been trepanning operations among men of the Reindeer Age and the Polished Stone Age. Medical opinion is far from unanimous about the origin and antiquity of syphilis. One thing is incontestable: it has existed in Europe since the fifteenth century and its spread closely followed the discovery of the New World by Christopher Columbus. It was in 1492 that he reached America; it was in 1493 that the first case of syphilis was observed in Spain and in 1495 that it made its appearance in Italy, in Naples to be exact. From Italy syphilis reached France at the beginning of the sixteenth century, following Charles VIII's campaigns in Italy, so that the French used to speak in those days of "the Naples evil" and the Italians, beaten in every field, expressed their rancour by speaking of "the French evil." Thereafter syphilis spread throughout Europe and was generously exported to Africa and Asia.

On the other hand, it is impossible to find, either on the Egyptian mummies or on the skeletons of Ancient Greece and Roman Italy, one indisputable symptom of the disease. Two theories continue in opposition: for some, syphilis has existed since prehistoric times and had remained more or less virulent until a clear recrudescence showed up under the action of the particularly evil American *Treponema pallidum;* for others, syphilis was unknown in the ancient world or in the Middle Ages and was imported from America following its conquest by the Spaniards. The bony lesions that can be observed on prehistoric skeletons or those dating from Greco-Roman times are always equivocal and do not allow us to come down on one side or the other.

In fact it is solely from a study of bony lesions that a history of the diseases of fossil man can be sketched. But the repercussions of a disease on the hardest and apparently the most static parts of an individual are much more numerous than is imagined. Thus we know with certainty that many of our distant ancestors were attacked by arthritis. For arthritis has attacked animals and men for thousands and thousands of years. Nothing is new under the sun and the oldest known case of arthritis is that of a *Diplodocus* that lived some 200 million years ago. Arthritis very often leaves traces on the bones: sometimes it is by the deformation and wear of contiguous articulating surfaces, and sometimes by the inflammation of the articular ligaments resulting in their ossification and articular ankylosis. Sometimes it is by the appearance of bony excrescences which, in the case of the vertebral column, end by joining up and forming a single hard block of bone (spondylosis). Now precise research has shown that such changes in articulation and spondylosis are comparatively frequent in all the fossils of giant reptiles, wild animals and prehistoric men for 200 million years, in Asia and Africa as well as in Europe, and in tropical as well as polar regions. It is even possible to say that arthritis was abnormally frequent in the Polished Stone Age, during which it seems to have attacked 40 to 50 per cent of the population, while it has since been somewhat in regression and on an average attacks only 25 per cent of the present population.

On the other hand, rickets, like dental caries, seems to have been extremely rare. The same does not hold true of fractures, accidents which must have happened very often during hunting; but to judge by the callosities observed on the skeletons, one must conclude that a certain technique of fracture dressing had already been brought to a satisfactory state, a technique which included both the reduction of the fracture as well as keeping the injured limb in place.

*

Having stated the essentials of art and life in prehistoric times we must, to end this first section, attempt a general synthesis of the origins and evolutions of humanity.

CHAPTER IV

From African Apes to Modern Nations

THE Pharaohs of the XIIth Dynasty (Middle Empire), especially Sesostris II, were zealous reformers and very wise rulers, and were anxious to assure their lands a healthy economic prosperity. So they conceived the idea of methodically exploiting an old prehistoric habitat watered by an arm of the Nile. In the process, aided by a skilful system of canals and locks, they created an artificial oasis south-east of Cairo, which became one of the most fertile regions of Egypt and has remained so for 4,000 years. Simultaneously they made it possible for the paleontologists of the twentieth century to discover the first apes to inhabit our planet.

About 60 miles before it reaches Cairo, an arm of the Nile breaks away and, turning north-west, passes through a deep gorge in the mountains of Libya to discharge into Lake Karoun, known to the ancient Egyptians as Lake Merour. This lake, with the canals, fields and woods that surround it, is the work of the Pharaohs of the XIIth Dynasty. The farmers who settled at the artificial oasis of Fayoum soon became numerous. Sesostris II himself lived there in an immense palace in the town of Shedet, consecrated to the crocodile-god Sebek, whence the name Crocodilopolis given it by the Greek historian Herodotus. The oasis has been continuously inhabited ever since, and has not failed to attract the attention of paleontologists, prehistorians and archaeologists, who have made there some very interesting discoveries. We shall soon have to discuss the fauna of Fayoum at some length; there the ancestors of elephants and rhinoceroses abounded, side by side with those of the great apes and perhaps of men. It is enough for the moment to note that in this part of Africa, 35 to 45 million years ago, there lived the first of all the known apes, discovered by an Austrian, Max Schlosser, in 1910.

Of this *Parapithecus* only the lower jaw was found, but the size of the jaw, the shape of the teeth, and the mode of their implantation provide valuable information. *Parapithecus*, which was scarcely larger than a marmoset, had a dental pattern identical to that of modern man with (for the half-jaw) two incisors, one canine, two pre-molars and three molars; moreover, judging from their general appearance and the number of roots on the molars, these teeth seemed as capable of evolving into human teeth as into those of the great anthropoid apes of to-day. Thus, by the close study of a single lower jaw that can be held in the hollow of a hand, the paleontologists can claim to have found one of the ancestral forms—the oldest yet known—of the anthropoid group from which at a certain stage the human line branched off. Fur-

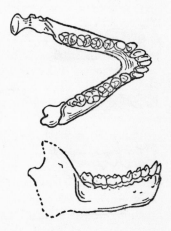

FIG. 48. Lower jaw of *Parapithecus*, with strongly humanized teeth.

thermore, certain features of the teeth of *Parapithecus* are very similar to those of the curious arboreal and nocturnal animals of Madagascar and the Sunda Islands, the lemurs and tarsiers, which will shortly be shown to us as the ancestors of the upper primates, apes and men.

Besides *Parapithecus*, Schlosser discovered at Fayoum the jaw of another and bigger ape, *Propliopithecus*, a probable descendant of *Parapithecus*. Thus, *Propliopithecus* enables us to establish a direct connection between the oldest known ape of Fayoum and the anthropoid apes discovered in Europe more than a century ago.

In fact, in 1834 Edouard Lartet had discovered, not far from his property at Sansan (Haute-Garonne), a very rich bed in which

the bones of elephants and the remains of apes that had lived in
the south of France some 30 million years ago were found side by
side. Lartet was thus able to describe to the Academy of Science
in 1837 a very primitive ape which he called *Pliopithecus;* later, in
1856, he was able to report on *Dryopithecus,* a little more recent
than the former, since the bed in which it was found gave it an
age of only 15 million years. These two papers, especially the
latter, had repercussions, for they suggested that Europe had once
been the habitat of great apes like gibbons, of which they were
moreover almost the direct ancestor; gibbons are to-day confined
to the Sunda Islands and to certain areas of South-east Asia. Above
all, Lartet and the paleontologist, Albert Gaudry, who had taken

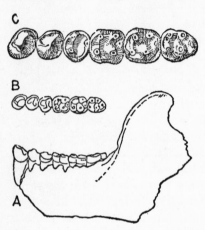

Fig. 49. Lower jaw of *Propliopithecus.*

part in the researches on *Dryopithecus,* could rightly emphasize
that the jaws of these apes showed some relationship to the human
jaw, mainly in the structure of the teeth.

Much more recently, excavations in Kenya have provided further
information regarding the occupation of the African continent
by apes several tens of millions of years ago. For some time a
famous British archaeologist, L. B. S. Leakey, was curator of the
Coridon Museum at Nairobi. But to his unquestionable qualifica-
tions in museum work he added an enthusiasm for fossils and
spent a great deal of his time in the bush with his wife, exploring
the paleontological beds of this region. In 1948, on the island of
Rusinga, in the southern part of Lake Victoria, Mrs. Leakey discovered the remains of a large ape rather "younger" than those

discovered at Fayoum, since it dated from only about 20 million years ago. This ape was called *Proconsul africanus*, as a tribute to the celebrated Consul, the most intelligent of the tame chimpanzees raised by the American zoologist Koehler. During recent years the discoveries made by Leakey in collaboration with Hopwood, have multiplied and to-day we have the remains of nearly 300 apes that inhabited Kenya at that epoch, some of the species represented being the size of a small gibbon, others being as big as a gorilla, while others come intermediate between those two extremes. Probably the most important of these simian species from Kenya is *Limnopithecus*, whose molars are very similar to human molars.

As a result of these discoveries, the genealogical tree of the earliest apes takes a fairly clear shape. It was in Egypt first of all, in the Fayoum region, that *Parapithecus* and *Propliopithecus* appeared. From the latter descended in more or less direct line the Kenya *Limnopithecus*, the European *Pliopithecus* (France, Switzerland, Bavaria, Slovakia, etc.) and the East African *Proconsul*. All these apes are remarkable for the shape of their teeth, which are not specialized, and especially for their canines, which are always of medium size as in men and never form fangs overlapping the other teeth as in the large apes of to-day. Furthermore, judging by the shape of their thigh and ankle-bones, these apes seem to have walked on their hind feet and to have used their arms little as a means of locomotion. Actually, the large apes of to-day generally move about by swinging from one branch to another with their arms, rather like trapezists: this is called brachiation. These ancient African apes show no sign of movement by brachiation or other adaptation to arboreal life.

So it was at this stage of evolution, let us say about 25 million years ago, that two branches seem to have definitely diverged from the stem of African apes, one leading in the direction of man and the other of modern apes, known as anthropoids, represented by the gibbons, chimpanzees, gorillas and orang-utans. It will therefore be well to examine the zoological place of both the great apes and man, paying as much attention to their differences as to their similarities.

*

First of all, both men and apes are mammals and within this animal class are grouped in an order very distinct from all others:

the primates. As mammals, men and apes are animals with hair-covered bodies that drop their young after a rather long gestation in the mother's womb, and after the birth suckle their young at the breast for a rather long period. Finally, they are warm-blooded animals with a constant internal temperature.

As to the primates themselves, it is rather difficult to define them in simple terms. To the layman the distinctive characteristics

FIG. 50. Spectral tarsier, *Tarsius*, from the East Indies. (Reproduced from Young's *Life of the Vertebrates*, Oxford Univ. Press.)

of this order might seem rather paltry; in fact, the primates are not very specialized, good for everything and good for nothing, to use a familiar expression. It is almost classic in this respect to recall the following anecdote related by Diogenes. Plato was asked for a definition of man and had replied: "He is an animal on two feet, but without feathers." Then Diogenes seized a cock, plucked it and presented it with the words, "Here is Plato's man." But Plato, not in the least put out, corrected his definition, "Man is an animal on two feet, without feathers, but with flat nails." This tale is something of a caricature, but it has the merit of clearly emphasizing the difficulties encountered in trying to define the primates. In the long run it is by observing the facts from the point of view of evolution that one can best make the typical characteristics of this order clear.

The "imperfect" apes are included in the order of primates—apes with dog-like muzzles, the zoologist's lemurians—still to be found to-day in Indo-Malaysia and Madagascar. The "perfect"

FIG. 51. Ring-tailed lemur, *Lemur catta*, from Madagascar. (From Young's *Life of the Vertebrates*, Oxford Univ. Press.)

apes are also included: capuchins, macacques, baboons, cynocephali, etc.—details of the classification of which will be given later. The "more-than-perfect" apes, if we can use the term, are included too: chimpanzees, orang-utans, gorillas and gibbons. These are so similar to man in their mimicry and their capacity to learn that they are grouped under the name of anthropoid apes. Finally, we include man.

Now the lemurians evolved first, then the apes, then the anthropoids, and finally man. One is therefore faced during this evolutionary progression with two simultaneous phenomena: the progressive development of the brain and the progressive loss of the natural means of defence. From the lemurs to man, the brain and cerebellum continually increase in volume and become more complicated through the development of cerebral convolutions and the physiological specialization of the various regions of the brain: there is progressive brain-development.

On the other hand and parallel to this, the specialized organs of defence have regressed, and this is an extremely important phenomenon. In that endless struggle for life that is the evolution of the living world, the acquisition or retention of the means of defence is an imperious necessity. Now defence can take various forms, sometimes by forestalling and passing at once to the attack, sometimes by seeking safety in flight, and sometimes by merely resisting the attacks of strangers. Thus, as natural means of defence, the carnivores have teeth and claws (they are the first to attack); elephants and rhinoceroses have horns (they resist when attacked); horses and ruminants try to save themselves by the swift use of their limbs. The existence in all groups of mammals of an adaptation to the struggle for life is thus revealed. Now with the primates there is nothing so clear: the five-toed feet do not make rapid flight or deep wounding possible; and in apes and men claws are replaced by flat finger-nails of doubtful efficacy. The teeth are of medium size and can produce formidable bites, but beginning with certain developed apes, the anthropoids and man, their number decreases from 36 to 32 and in the human branch they decrease also in size. On the other hand, many apes know how to use sticks and other projectiles to defend themselves; with the human branch the use of weapons has definitely prevailed. Thus the primates offer no remarkable anatomical characteristic except for the development of the cranium, demonstrating an increase in brain-power to which is associated the intelligent use of various instruments making possible a successful struggle against competition from other animal species.

But within the order of primates man seems like a being apart and, after having clearly fixed his place beside the apes, it is important now to distinguish him from them, and more especially from the anthropoids. The first essential difference bears upon the great development of the human cranium; in fact, on the development of his brain. In the course of evolution, this growth of the cranium occurs at the expense of the face. Is there any need to describe an ape's head with its large projecting face and its flat skull in order to contrast it with a man's head, with its relatively flat face and a cranium that is both tall and bulges at the back above the nape? It is in its facial projection that the strongly prognathous apes clearly differ from man with his orthognathous features. Cuvier put it thus: "Of all animals man is the one with the largest cranium and the smallest face, and animals differ the more from these proportions as they become more stupid and ferocious."

Since Cuvier's day, however, the mathematical interpretation

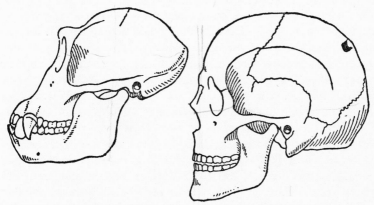

FIG. 52. Anatomical differences between a human skull (*right*) and an anthropoid skull (*left*).

of scientific observation has assumed great importance; the differences between craniums are now expressed in very precise fashion with the help of two figures called the cephalic index and the cranial capacity. The cephalic index (I) is obtained by multiplying by 100 the greatest width of the cranium (*l*) and dividing the product by the length of the cranium (L), this being expressed by the equation: $I = \dfrac{l \times 100}{L}$

The variations of this cephalic index allow us to class craniums into three categories: dolicocephalic, familiarly known as "long headed," the cephalic index being below 77.77; brachycephalic or "round headed," with a cephalic index above 80; finally, average skulls, the mesaticephalic, with a cephalic index between 77.77

and 80. The anthropoids and the most distant ancestors of man are all dolicocephalic. It was very late in the process of human evolution that the round heads appeared.

Cranial capacity is only the expression in cubic centimetres of the content of the brain-pan. This figure therefore gives—indirectly, but very precisely—an indication of the volume of the brain. The cranial capacity of the great apes is about 500 c.c. and of modern man about 1,300 c.c.

It is important to note, furthermore, that man, having articulate

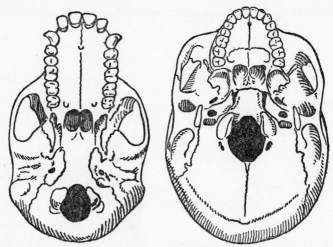

FIG. 53. Anatomical differences between the U-shaped dental arcade of an anthropoid (*left*), with projecting canines and a space where the opposing canine fits, and the dental arcade of a man (*right*). The foramen magnum is situated towards the back in the anthropoid, while it is in an almost central position in man.

speech, shows a special anatomy of the tongue and certain organs surrounding the tongue, which must be able to move freely; also of the parts of the brain corresponding to the functions of speech. The anthropoids are further distinguished from men by their dental anatomy: their canines are very developed, extending far beyond the level of the other teeth and touching the gums of the opposing jaw; such development of the canines, especially marked among the males, involves a gap (a diastema) between the last incisor and the first molar of the opposite jaw. Nothing like this occurs in man.

Finally, although the anthropoids and man assume a more or less vertical posture, in practice the large apes generally move as quadrupeds, almost always supporting themselves with their long arms. The arms are also used for progressing from branch to branch (brachiation).

An upright posture raises the serious problem of maintaining the head in equilibrium at the top of the vertebral column. The brain connects with the spinal cord through an orifice in the base of the skull known as the foramen magnum. In man this is situated in a horizontal plane, since the spinal cord detaches itself perpendicularly from the brain and the head is perched in equilibrium at

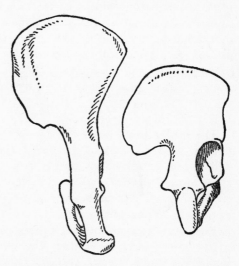

FIG. 54. Diagnostic anatomical differences in the pelvises of anthropoid (*left*; long, narrow and relatively slender) and man (*right*; broad, splayed and relatively squat).

the top of the column; in the anthropoids, on the contrary, the head inclines forward and the orifice is placed in a more or less oblique plane from back to front. The foramen magnum is thus a really valuable factor to study, for its position gives a vital indication of the normal posture and method of locomotion. Another essential indication of whether an animal had a vertical or an inclined posture is given by the structure of the pelvic bones: in man, the pelvis is enlarged and widened, supporting the whole weight of the abdominal organs; but in the anthropoids, the pelvis only assumes this function to a slight degree and is definitely narrower and longer than in man.

Finally, in the great apes, the big toe can be made to face the

other toes, a peculiarity which has often caused the anthropoids
to be known by the otherwise incorrect name "quadrumana."

In this way the close study of a few pieces of bone can inform
the specialists of the anatomical and physiological peculiarities of
fossils. Simply by considering the position of the foramen magnum and the shape of the pelvis, anthropologists can decide with
great certainty whether the creature under examination was a
biped or a quadruped; with nothing but the cephalic index and
the cranial capacity, within the margin of the 1,300 c.c. for man
and 500 c.c. for the great apes, they can relate the fossil to either
one or the other; with nothing to consider but the shape of the
teeth and the development of the canines they can form an idea
of the relationship to either anthropoids or man. The thickness
of the bones, the shape of the orbits, the anatomy of the cavity
of the ear, and many other details give the anthropologist,
paleontologist and prehistorian exact and valuable data for re-
tracing the conquest of the world by the human species.

*

The reader now knows enough for an attempt to present him
with a five-act drama in the purest classical tradition, though it
will unfortunately be impossible to respect the sacred law of the
three unities, since the action takes place over hundreds of thousands of years and at various points of the globe. This tragi-
comedy in five acts has a very attractive title: "The Adventure of
Humanity." The authors are numerous and the most important
of them—Boucher de Perthes, Casimir Picard, Lartet, Marcellin
Boule, the Abbé Breuil, Teilhard de Chardin, Vallois, Schlosser,
Leakey, Dart, Broom, Dubois, Black, Weidenreich, von Koenigswald, and all the others that we cannot mention here—have been
presented during the long prologue which is at last coming to
an end.

When the curtain rises on the first act, some small apes, scarcely
larger than one's two fists—*Parapithecus*—occupy the stage. They
lived in a region with a moderately warm climate, rather like that
of the Mediterranean to-day; this region—the future Egyptian
oasis of Fayoum—was situated almost at the shore of the Mediterranean Sea, then much larger than it is today and stretching like
a belt around three-quarters of the globe. This was the geologists'
Oligocene, which began 45 million years ago and lasted for 10

COMPARISON BETWEEN MEN AND ANTHROPOIDS	
MEN	**ANTHROPOIDS**
Large cranium and reduced face	Flattened cranium and projecting face
Three types of cranium	Always dolicocephalic
Brain of from 1,300 to 1,600 c.c.	Brain of from 400 to 600 c.c.
Superciliary arches effaced	Brow ridge above the orbits
Mandible of small strength	Very strong mandible
Chin	No chin
Hyperbolical or parabolical dental arch	U-shaped dental arcade
Non-projecting canines (thus no diastema)	Projecting canines, especially in the male (diastema in consequence)
Vertebral column in three curves	Vertebral column in two curves
Short fore-limbs	Long fore-limbs

RESEMBLANCES
Tendency to straighten the body
Tendency to walk on two legs
Development of the brain and intelligence

DEFINITELY HUMAN FEATURES
Articulate speech
Great intellectual qualities
Vertical posture
Functional differentiation of hands and feet

million years. But at the end of this period *Parapithecus* was soon replaced by its descendant, *Propliopithecus,* a sort of small gibbon, scarcely 3 feet tall.

Soon the scene changes to the Miocene (which covered the period from 35 million to 15 million years ago): other apes that descended direct from *Propliopithecus* have left the region in Egypt where they arose and have invaded Europe and Africa. Some were more or less like gorillas, some more or less like chimpanzees; they were the Kenya *Proconsul, Pliopithecus* in France (especially at Sansan in Haute-Garonne), Switzerland, Slovakia, Bavaria, and finally and above all, *Limnopithecus* in South-east Africa. This last anthropoid is especially interesting, since it seems to have given birth to the principal actors of the next scene, the ape-men of South Africa, discovered and studied by Dart, Broom and the English anatomist, Le Gros Clark.

*

When the curtain rises on the second act, the scene is a plain at the edge of the Kalahari desert. Bordering the desert on the north are great limestone cliffs; water-courses run along their feet and on the banks of these are the few trees of the region. The climate is hot and humid. In this land lived antelopes and jumping hares, badgers, giant moles and several species of those small apes we now know as baboons; in the rivers were fresh-water crabs, turtles and numerous fish. But the most important animal of the region, the principal actor in this Pliocene period, which covered 10 million years, was the ape-man, *Australopithecus*.

Physically *Australopithecus* was a creature of very modest size, about 40 to 48 inches tall, but—an innovation in the animal world —he moved about on his hind feet: he had acquired an upright posture. Seen from a distance, *Australopithecus* was already an agile little man, hairy and bent slightly forwards; but at close range he still looked like an ape with his projecting face, his projecting and beetling brow and his flattened cranium. *Australopithecus* lived in bands and seemed to co-operate with its fellows in procuring food. Dart, who devoted 30 years of his scientific career to its study, imagines them encircling herds of antelopes around a water-hole and the most skilful of them felling their prey with stones and sticks. Dart sees them also digging in the earth, sometimes with sticks and sometimes with large pointed stones, to open up the burrows and so capture the giant moles and jumping hares. Finally, it is almost certain that *Australopithecus* cared very little for its kinship with the baboons that abounded in the region, and felled them by blows with sticks at the nape of the neck.

All these prey, as well as fresh-water crabs and turtles which were gathered at the river banks, were then transported to the caves in the limestone cliffs where *Australopithecus* lived. There antelopes, baboons, moles, crabs, hares, and turtles were consumed after having been roughly skinned with the aid of naturally sharpened but deliberately collected stones. It is not possible to state that the meat was cooked before being eaten, although Dart claims to have found traces of hearths in the caves of *Australopithecus;* other authors quite as competent deny the authenticity of these hearths.

Anyhow, in the caves of *Australopithecus* are found numerous bones from animals that served them as food and especially many baboon craniums, fractured at the base as if they had been struck there. It has sometimes been maintained that these fractures resulted from accidental falls; but the hypothesis is difficult to sustain, since one can scarcely imagine an epidemic of suicide or

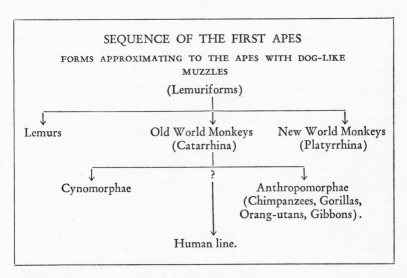

SEQUENCE OF THE FIRST APES

FORMS APPROXIMATING TO THE APES WITH DOG-LIKE MUZZLES

(Lemuriforms)

| Lemurs | Old World Monkeys (Catarrhina) | New World Monkeys (Platyrrhina) |

| Cynomorphae | ? | Anthropomorphae (Chimpanzees, Gorillas, Orang-utans, Gibbons). |

Human line.

clumsiness affecting so many baboons in the Kalahari desert, especially as baboons never climb trees and the region anyway contained nothing bigger than herbaceous plants and small bushes.

At the same time, a descendant of *Proconsul, Dryopithecus,* much more ape and much less man, and already tending towards modern types of anthropoid (gorillas, gibbons and chimpanzees), had invaded the rest of the world: France, Slovakia, Africa, and the Siwalik hills of India. In this latter region of hills and low mountains that form a vestibule to the Himalayas, very many apes have been found over the last 30 years, that have been given such evocative names as *Ramapithecus, Bramapithecus, Sivapithecus, Sugrivapithecus;* they were found side by side with some species of *Dryopithecus.* However, these anthropoids are closer to man than are chimpanzees or gorillas. It is important to note the existence of this sub-division of the ape-group in process of evolving towards a fairly human type, for there are probably many more discoveries to be made in the Siwaliks; further fossils, even more human, might well be extracted in years to come, and some years ago the geologist, de Terra, when considering the different parts of the world which could have served as the cradle of humanity, finally eliminated all except the Siwalik region.

*

Now comes the third act. The scene moves to China, but it closely resembles the preceding one in the sense that here too limestone hills, hollowed out into deep caves, form the northern boundary of a desert region where the vegetation is rather poor. But time has passed: it is now the period known as the Lower Paleolithic, only some hundreds of thousands of years ago (extending from 500,000 to 100,000 years before our time). In the plain lived an extremely varied fauna: rhinoceroses, horses, sheep, bison, camels of great size, buffalos, elephants, and deer with very large and very flat antlers, while carnivorous beasts, bears and sabre-toothed tigers sheltered in the caves, as well as a hyena of great size which was very numerous throughout the region. But the wild beasts had to share these caves with the Pekin man, the man-ape of China, *Sinanthropus.*

This time we are faced with creatures of medium height, from 4 feet 11 inches to 5 feet 3 inches, who used only their lower limbs to move about and were probably very agile, though they still had much of the ape in their prognathous faces, in the ridge above the eyes, their flat craniums and the ridge above the nape. As far as we can judge, they were bent earthwards and their legs were bowed. On the other hand, the Pekin man was right-handed; for, according to mouldings of the cranial cavity, the left cerebral hemisphere seems always, as in modern man, more developed than the right, and we know that the muscle movements of the right side of the body are governed by the left half of the brain and *vice versa.*

In hunting, which they probably pursued in more or less numerous parties and perhaps under the direction of hunters more skilful than the rest, *Sinanthropus* used weapons of chipped stone, fairly numerous specimens having been found in the caves; they perhaps used sticks too. All the animals of the neighbourhood were their prey, but we are by no means sure that the most important and the most sought-after of these prey was not *Sinanthropus* himself. In fact, the few long bones of the arm and leg that have been found in the caves of *Sinanthropus*—to be exact, a fragment of femur, a half-broken clavicle and two pieces of humerus—were all broken at the ends, as if an attempt had been made to extract the marrow; some even show traces of calcination. Finally, all these bones—pieces of skull, teeth, pieces of limb—were piled haphazardly with the bones of other animals, just as in a kitchen midden; there is no question of voluntary burial as with other prehistoric men. The paleontologists have quite naturally come to the conclusion that, to be thus mutilated, *Sinanthropus* must have served as prey to creatures who could only have been others of his kind from a neighbouring tribe. A few paleontologists, it is true, have claimed that a real man had lived in the caves of Choukoutien at the same time as *Sinanthropus*, whose favourite prey he was; but it has never been possible to find the least relic of this hypothetical human being. Other paleontologists, refusing to admit that one of our ancestors, however distant, could have devoured his own kind, have accused the comparatively enormous hyenas that swarmed at Choukoutien of having broken the Pekin man's bones. However, the majority of experts adopt the hypothesis that *Sinanthropus* had cannibal tendencies.

Even though he has not, unfortunately, taken the trouble to leave indisputable records to his descendants, it is easy to imagine the Pekin man hunting his too adventurous or too aggressive neighbours; after having killed them with blows from stones or sticks, he quickly took from the still warm corpse the pieces that were reputed for their flavour or for their magic properties, especially the marrow of the long bones (which explains why the long bones in the caves are very few). Then, to return to his cave. *Sinanthropus* loaded himself only with the heads and a few easily carried "beefsteaks and roasts." The accumulation of craniums in the caves of Choukoutien can also have another meaning: they can be regarded as hunting trophies, or better (since they are almost always broken in such a way that the dome is clearly separated from the face and base of the cranium) as domestic utensils, serving as receptacles in an epoch when the invention of pottery was still a long way off. Also, this breaking of the craniums could very well have taken place during magical ceremonies accompanying the eating of the brain. All of which is naturally in the realm of hypothesis. Nonetheless, the bones found piled up in the former hearths of *Sinanthropus* are strangely like the kitchen refuse of the rare anthropophagous man of to-day, for example the Kanakas. However, we need not go so far as to believe that *Sinanthropus* was uncompromisingly carnivorous: he also consumed currants and bilberries, as proved by the fossilized seeds of these plants found in fairly large numbers in the Chinese caves.

However severe the judgment we might make on the tastes of *Sinanthropus* in the matter of food, at least he knew how to shape the implements that ensured his food. By striking blocks of quartz with sticks or stones he detached splinters from the central nucleus and used either these splinters, roughly touched up at the edges, or the nucleus itself, made a little sharper. It was an industry neither of splinters nor nuclei, but a very primitive basic type. It is generally reckoned that the Pekin man also broke certain bones to use them as weapons or as implements for cutting up carcasses; the horns and long bones of deer seemed to have been preferred.

Nothing precise can be said of the mental activities of this man-ape, other than that he seems to have possessed a very rudimentary language, as evidenced by certain marks of muscular insertions on the skulls.

But now the scene broadens and gains in depth; while the Pekin men continued to devour one another in northern China, other pre-men, comparable to them anatomically, physiologically and mentally, if not completely identical, appeared in the Sunda Islands (Dubois' and von Koenigswald's *Pithecanthropus*). Also, in South Africa, *Africanthropus*, of which nearly 200 small bone fragments have been collected since 1935; patiently reassembled, these form two flat and long cranial domes with strongly projecting brow and occipital ridges, a few isolated teeth and a few remains of the upper jaw. This was a very advanced type of man, almost a Neanderthal man. Evidence of these pre-men eventually turned up in Europe in the Mauer jaw-bone, which deserves some attention.

Dr. Otto Schoetensack, reader in geology at Heidelberg University, one day discovered that the nearby gravel-pits contained very interesting animal fossils: horses, wild bison, dogs, cats, lions, beavers, elephants and rhinoceroses. It occurred to Schoetensack that human remains might be found there some day. So every day he covered the 12 miles from Heidelberg to the little village of Mauer and back, and with the permission of the proprietor of the quarry watched the men at work and himself dug a little. When he arrived there, on October 21st, 1907, the foreman held out to him the large jaw-bone that crowned his efforts. This jaw-bone had a very crude look; the bones were extremely thick and there was no chin. It was not unlike an ape's jaw, but an ape of

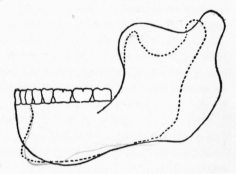

FIG. 55. The Mauer jaw-bone, the oldest European human relic, compared with a modern human jaw, indicated by the dotted line.

very great size. On the other hand, the teeth were practically identical with those of modern man. So it was a real pre-man who lived at this epoch in Europe, combining human and ape features, but different from both *Pithecanthropus* and *Sinanthropus*.

Nevertheless, the third act ends a hundred thousand years ago and allows the spectator to see the birth, at various points on the globe—Europe, Asia and Africa—of some pre-men, still slightly ape-like and not wholly men, but creatures who had nevertheless the gift of technical invention (they are often referred to as *Homo faber* to distinguish them from *Homo sapiens*) and the rudiments of spoken language.

*

With the fourth act the scene changes entirely. It is very cold everywhere. The glaciers stretch down from the north and from the high mountain chains, the Alps, Pyrenees and Himalayas, for the fourth time. In Europe they invade the plains, covering Holland and Belgium, the greater part of Germany, almost the whole of Switzerland and northern Italy. Elsewhere, around the tropics, endless rains flood the greater part of Africa and certain regions of Asia. In Europe a humid cold at first prevails; then an increasingly dry sharp frost. The wind sweeps across the glaciers, raising masses of yellow dust, minute grains of sand which accumulate in the steppes bordering the glacier front, forming a thickening carpet of what is known to geologists as the loess and to-day worked in very numerous sand-pits.

Descending from the north, fleeing before the extending ice, innumerable herds of reindeer, comprising thousands of creatures, less numerous herds of the great bog deer (or Irish deer) with their immense shovel-shaped antlers, marmots, arctic hares and blue foxes invaded our countries. During this time the fauna that occupied the temperate zone of Europe disappeared; thereafter the hippopotamus, elephant and Merck rhinoceros were then to be found only in Africa. The lions, bears and hyenas took refuge in the caves. Finally there appeared the great ungulates like the mammoth and the woolly rhinoceros, all of them being covered with a thick coat of long hair.

This was the epoch when, by necessity, man systematically began to take refuge in the caves which alone could give him shelter, sometimes precarious, from the rigours of the climate. In a few sentences, Bergounioux and Glory have made perfectly clear the consequences of these changes of temperature on the habitat and ways of prehistoric men:

"As soon as man occupied the floor of a shelter with a constant temperature, he built a hearth of large stones and heaped charcoal in it. Pell-mell, he piled up the debris of his stone industry (splinters, strikers, flint nodules) together with the broken bones of the fore- and hind-limbs of his prey killed during the preceding season's hunting. When the summer returned he left his shelter, sometimes for ever, and the hyenas came to gnaw the abandoned bones. Their coproliths (excrement impregnated with calcium phosphate) and the marks of their canines on the bones betray their presence. The unoccupied burrow filled up with fragments of rock that fell from the roof and walls as a result of the alternating phases of frost and thaw. The clays, silts and gravels brought by the trickling water formed an empty bed ready to

The grave of a Cro-Magnon man, discovered near Menton. The shells that surround the head and the foetal position of the body indicate the existence of a funerary cult in the Reindeer Age. (Musée de l'Homme, Paris.)

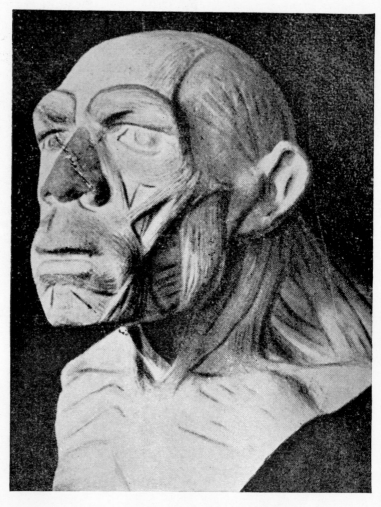

Reconstruction of the facial muscles of the
Neanderthal man. (Boule.)

receive new occupants. The thickness of this deposit varies according to the place and region: over 150 feet at Choukoutien (China), 56 feet at Castillo (Spain), 28 feet at Krapina (Croatia), and 15½ feet in the painted cave at Collias (Gard, France).

"The study of the superposition of layers with and without archaeological objects permit one to set up a rough chronology of the various industrial techniques."

At this period of human history the actors were very numerous: they were the Neanderthal men of Europe, Asia and South Africa. The Neanderthal man is adequately described by recalling his general brutish bearing, bandy legs, low shoulders and bent back, his prognathous face, receding forehead and eyes deeply sunk in their orbits and overhung by a large bony protuberance.

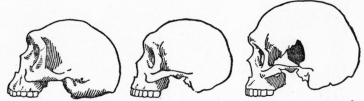

FIG. 56. Neanderthal skulls: (*left*) backward, (*centre*) average, (*right*) advanced.

Here, then, are the Neanderthal men making all sorts of implements out of chipped stone, as well as throwing weapons and tools for preparing, cleaning and sewing furs. And here they are, too, covering themselves with manganese dioxide and red ochre for some ritual ceremony, burying their dead, preparing for a hunt, or initiating the young hunters into the tribal mysteries.

It is especially interesting to see that anatomically it is possible to divide the Neanderthal men into two large groups. On the one hand there are, according to Father Teilhard de Chardin, the backward ones, the "savages" of the epoch; their skeletal characteristics are very like those of the last of the pre-men of Southeast Asia in that the cranium is flat, the forehead recedes, the face projects, and so on. These "savages" are the Java man and the Rhodesian man, as well as the man from the valley of the Neander, the first Neanderthal man to be discovered. On the other hand, in Palestine and in Germany lived the "advanced" Neanderthal

men, the "civilized" men of the epoch, with prominent cheek-
bones, a relatively tall forehead, a well-formed chin, and a face
that was a little less prognathous than in the average Neanderthal
men. It is a very curious fact, which the prehistorians have much
trouble in explaining, that among the oldest of the Neanderthalians, chronologically speaking, are those which show the "advanced" characteristics.

But, although the Neanderthal men were the principal and most
numerous actors, beside them and more discreetly, in some well-
defined regions, especially in Southern England and on the Atlantic
shores of France, other men were developing, notably the Swanscombe man and the Fontéchevade man.

Unfortunately, we know very little about them. These are in
fact only known by the tops of their craniums and by a few rare
fragments of face-bones. Yet they were undoubtedly attached to
the line of modern men: all the bones we possess of them (all
dated beyond dispute, since they have passed their flourine examination) are distinguished from the craniums of modern men
only by their greater thickness, by a greater width of the occipitals
(a tiny detail!) and perhaps by a certain flattening of the top of the
cranium.

It is known, too, that these men used worked stones and possessed five or six types of tools adapted to different purposes. But the
essential fact remains that these already modern men were contemporary with or even earlier than Neanderthal men.

*

This is the moment to pause briefly for a backward glance
before the curtain rises on the fifth act, in the course of which
men already anatomically modern take their place on the face of
the earth—the moment to attempt a general reconstitution of the
evolution of humanity.

We have now presented the four evolutionary stages from very
primitive apes to present-day men. In the first of these were un-
differentiated forms still similar to the lemurians and ready to
evolve in various directions; in fact from these, more or less directly, came the apes properly so-called, the anthropoids and the
human line. In the second stage were the small ape-men, the
Australopithecines of South Africa, in which the simian characteristics were still dominant, although the human characteristics—or,

at the very least, the humanoid—are already to be found, as well as a certain tendency to live in society and to use weapons and implements intelligently. In the third stage of the men-apes, the pre-men of South-east Asia and South Africa mingle human and simian anatomical features in almost equal parts; these were no longer real anthropoids but they were not yet men. Finally, to these creatures must be attributed a certain intelligence in the way of technique, as evidenced by their use of deliberately chipped stones. In the fourth stage appeared the Neanderthal man, a man beyond dispute (though his skeleton still showed certain primitive features). Besides a fair variety of tools, this man already had certain religious and magical customs and deliberately buried his dead.

From this zoological sequence some anthropologists have sought to construct an extremely simple genealogical tree of the human species; in recent years, the Czech professor of anatomy, Hrdlička, living in America, has come out in support of this over-simplification, which makes modern man descend directly from the Neanderthal man, the Neanderthal man from the last of the pre-men, and the pre-men from *Australopithecus*—at the cost of unimaginable migrations of which one has not the slightest proof.

In fact, when one tries to begin constructing a genealogical tree of the human species, one has to take into account the fact that fossil men, very different from one another anatomically and mentally, were contemporary with one another or practically so. For example, we have already learnt of the simultaneous existence of the Mauer man and the pre-men, or of certain Neanderthal men and the men of Fontéchevade. So it is important to agree here and now on certain indisputable points.

The first fact on which we might agree is that the ancestors of man were born of primitive ape-like forms which, if they were not necessarily *Parapithecus* and *Propliopithecus*, must at least have strongly resembled them. Thereafter, certain of these forms were progressively "humanized." Some anatomical features remained practically unchanged, as was largely the case with the shape of the teeth; other anatomical features were slowly transformed, as was the case with the cranial dome and the progressive reduction of the occipital and brow ridges. Furthermore, certain psycho-physiological adaptations took place: the cranial capacity increased, the pattern of the cerebral convolutions became more complicated, all this being correlated to what must be called, in default of a better term, the development of the intelligence, which showed up in the invention of weapons and implements that slowly but steadily assured man an even greater supremacy over the external world.

The stages that marked these transformations are as follows: the ape-man stage (Australopithecines), and then the man-ape stage (Mauer man and *Pithecanthropus*). Once more, this does not mean that *Australopithecus* was the direct ancestor of the ape-man of Asia, any more than that *Pithecanthropus* and *Sinanthropus* were the direct ancestors of modern man. We have finally to admit our ignorance—undoubtedly only temporary—of the exact system of relationships between these various stages. But it can meanwhile be stated that the direct ancestors of modern man, though they were not necessarily *Australopithecus* and *Pithecanthropus*, must have strongly resembled them, bringing together certain features which are still those of modern man and certain other features that are the attributes of the anthropoids.

But the problem of the Neanderthal man is rather special. For a long time there was a temptation to regard him as a fourth stage, succeeding the man-ape stage and leading towards the modern fossil men of the Reindeer Age, since he was a little less an ape and a little more a man than the Asian and African *Pithecanthropus*. But here we must take account of the fact that the Neanderthal men were contemporaries of men already modern at least as regards their craniums.

All the experts to-day agree that the Neanderthal man is what we can call a relic; in other words, when the Neanderthal men vanished from the surface of the earth they did not survive in any direct descendant. On the other hand, almost contemporary with them there were already some prehuman and human forms that gave rise to modern humanity: the men of Swanscombe and Fontéchevade. This amounts to saying that life has made at least two attempts in the human direction: one, the Neanderthal attempt, which came to grief, and the other, the Swanscombe-Fontéchevade attempt, which succeeded. But in default of new discoveries that can provide us with other information than the anatomy of their craniums, nothing permits us yet to state that the Swanscombe-Fontéchevade line might itself be the origin of modern man. Perhaps there were not only two but many more attempts in the direction of man.

This phenomenon is not exceptional in paleontology; it has long been familiar in other animal lines more prolific in fossil forms, like horses, rhinoceroses, elephants, and a great number of invertebrates. What would have been exceptional is that the contrary had been the case and that one could have set up a direct relationship between the ancestors of apes and man, without the development of parallel lines that came to nothing.

For we must take into account also the existence of the progressive Neanderthal men; these very ancient men could well have been at the origin of the fossil and modern races, so that between the progressive Neanderthalians (the oldest) and the backward Neanderthalian (the most recent) there was perhaps no direct relationship at all.

Now is the moment to sketch the genealogical tree of the human species, so far as present knowledge permits. To construct this tree we must call upon the theories of the leading experts of the day, especially those of Boule and Vallois, Father Teilhard de Chardin, d'Arambourg, de Furon and the British anatomist, Le Gros Clark.

Everyone is more or less agreed about that part of the tree that leads from *Parapithecus* to *Australopithecus*, and discussion concerns only points of detail of little importance to the layman. But once the *Australopithecus* stage is reached argument is much more lively. The various views that have been held on this subject must therefore be presented. They can be roughly grouped into four main hypotheses.

The first hypothesis, which is only mentioned here as a reminder, is Hrdlička's; he makes the four principal stages in the evolution of humanity descend directly one from another. This hypothesis is very difficult to maintain in the present state of our knowledge.

The second hypothesis makes the Mauer man descend almost directly from the *Australopithecus*, and from him modern man descends through the Swanscombe-Fontéchevade line. On the other side, the pre-men and the Neanderthal men have also descended from *Australopithecus*, evolving independently, though they were more or less rapidly extinguished without leaving survivors.

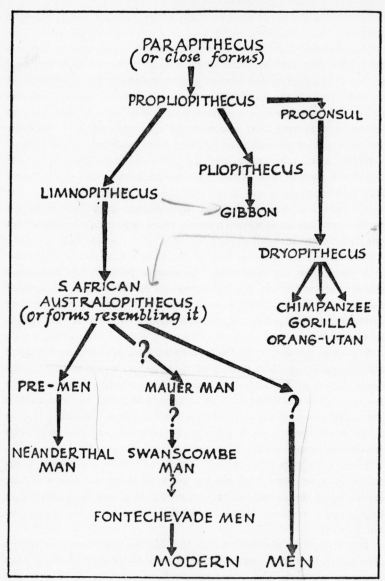

Attempt at a Genealogical Tree of Man

In the third hypothesis the Mauer man is still at the origin of modern man, but this time by way of the progressive Neanderthal men (the oldest). On their side, and still more or less deriving from *Australopithecus*, came first of all the pre-men, who gave rise to the typical Neanderthalians. The Swanscombe-Fontéchevade line evolved independently, though no one knows its origin or end.

The fourth hypothesis admits purely and simply that at least four attempts have been made in the human direction: *Australopithecus*, pre-man, the Neanderthal man, and finally modern man, the last having alone succeeded. In this hypothesis it could equally well have been in the Swanscombe-Fontéchevade line that modern man had his origin.

All this is summarized in the accompanying table, which presents a schematic view of these various hypotheses, of which only the second and third appear to have been confirmed by later discoveries.

So as regards the origins of humanity it is necessary to confine oneself in the end to the following outline: from the anatomical point of view, four evolutionary stages followed one another, and from one to the other the individuals increasingly approximated to *Homo sapiens*. But intricacies and ramifications developed at the different stages and it has to be admitted that several attempts in the direction of man took place, only one of which succeeded. Once again this parallel evolution is not exceptional: on the contrary, it is to be found in all the animal groups and it would be abnormal if it had not occurred during human evolution.

Thus an attempt at a precise reconstitution of the origins of humanity should close on a note of interrogation. We must be content with a general outline, which later discoveries may bring to completion; paleontological activity throughout the world in recent years allows us to hope that they will not be long delayed.

✻

But to bring this problem of the origin of man to a conclusion, two questions remain which fall within the province of biology and paleontology. The first concerns the biological mechanism by which the ape, or more precisely the pre-anthropoid, was able to transform itself into man. The other concerns the cradle of humanity.

A certain number of biologists, following the Dutchman Bolk,

are at present inclined to suggest as a substitute for the expression
"man is descended from the ape" (for which there is not the least
justification) the expression "man is descended from the fetus of
the ape." In actual fact, all things considered, there is more
resemblance between a human fetus and an anthropoid fetus than
between an adult man and an adult anthropoid; and man himself,
with his large head, and a cranium which has developed to the
detriment of the face, his relative absence of hair, the late cutting
of his teeth, his protracted ossification (resulting in very long
growth which scarcely ends before the 25th year, when the long
bones cease to increase in length), offers a certain number of
characteristics which in other animals are only to be found in the
fetus. This theory is the more attractive since it can be biologically
explained.

In 1864 the armies of Napoleon III were carrying on a luckless
war in Mexico. One day a military doctor sent the Minister for
Foreign Affairs some 30 creatures which had been taken from the
lakes of this part of Mexico; they were batrachians resembling
newts or salamanders, with a long and rather flat tail and a collar
of filamentous gills, which serve to absorb the oxygen from the
water. These animals were known by the name given them by
the natives of the region: axolotls. Much embarrassed, the Minister
gave them to the Zoological Society; the Society kept a certain
number and offered six to the Natural History Museum. These
were immediately taken over by a famous naturalist named
Auguste Duméril, who for seven years had held the chair in the
zoology of reptiles and fishes. This gift gave Duméril the opportunity to study the habits, food, and reproduction of these curious
creatures, which had many offspring. In fact, shortly after their
arrival, in February 1865, several little axolotls were born whose
later conduct rather discountenanced the experts. In the autumn
of the same year these little axolotls of six months suddenly began
to lose their gills and part of their tails, and to turn into brown
salamanders with yellow spots, emerging from the water and taking up residence on the fine sand at the edge of the aquarium.

This gave Duméril the opportunity to carry out the most interesting investigations of his career, resulting in conclusions of
considerable importance to biology. These famous yellow-spotted
salamanders were in fact already fairly well known to the zoologists, who had given them the scientific name of *Amblystoma*.

Knowing the mode of development of the batrachians, which always pass, after leaving the egg, through an aquatic "tadpole" phase before changing into adults, which sometimes remain aquatic (newts) and sometimes become terrestrial (toads, frogs, salamanders), Duméril was quite naturally led to the conclusion that the axolotls sent from Mexico were none other than the larvae— that is to say, the tadpoles—of *Amblystoma*. The fact in itself was not very surprising, but what was more surprising was that the axolotls reproduced themselves in the larval stage.

Duméril continued his observations for several years and discovered that certain animals are able to reproduce themselves in the larval state, thus giving birth to larvae which resemble them in every way. This phenomenon was thoroughly studied in 1886 by the German Kollmann, who gave it the name neoteny. Neoteny is found among numerous parasitical worms, where one can observe several generations of larvae succeed one another before the appearance of the adult generation; also among certain insects. However, neoteny is exceptional among batrachians; it is explained in the case of the axolotls by the iodine content of water, iodine being absolutely necessary to the metamorphosis of axolotls into *Amblystoma*, a thing that happens fairly rarely in the mountain pools of Mexico, where these creatures normally live.

Thus by reference to neotenous phenomena it is sought to make man, with his fetus-like characteristics, descend from animal forms similar to the ancestors of the anthropoids. Under the influence of some factor that naturally cannot yet be precisely defined, but which might well be the result of some hormonal disequilibrium, a primitive anthropoid might have acquired the ability to reproduce itself at the larval stage. Such a theory, without any proof so far, at present interests a certain number of experts and all interpretations of the origins of humanity must take it into account. Meanwhile, it would be stupid to seek to push things to the extreme, by making modern man descend from the Neanderthal man by neoteny, and the Neanderthal man from the man-ape by the same process, and the latter from the *Australopithecus*.

All such characteristics as the reduction of the hair system and the late cutting of teeth require that man effected the first steps of his evolution in a relatively warm if not tropical climate, especially because for food he had to reckon on the presence of plants throughout the year, since his prey could not be regularly assured. So we reach the problem of humanity's birthplace. Agreement is almost unanimous in siting the birthplace in the warm regions of the globe, but some paleontologists favour Asia (the Siwaliks) while others favour Africa (Kenya or the Transvaal). Broom's recent discoveries, which show *Australopithecus* in full evolution, at present lead many experts to consider tropical Africa as pre-eminently the cradle of primitive humanity. On the other hand, the partisans of Asia insist on the fact that the high plateaus close to the Himalaya, which occupy the center of the Asiatic continent, some millions of years ago had a much milder climate than that which prevails to-day. They also point out that only one scientific expedition has yet worked in these regions, and that it had to work very quickly and in very precarious conditions.

*

So modern man made his appearance on the earth for the first time at the beginning of the Reindeer Age. Modern he was in his general anatomy but, in the fifth and last act of humanity's adventure, he was already split up into races, though they are not identical with those of to-day.

The other feature typical of this last act is the appearance of art for the first time in history, manifesting itself in engravings, paintings and sculptures, executed either on the walls of caves, flat stones or pieces of bone. Technical acquirements were also very considerable, and the implements made of chipped stone and bone were very varied.

The climate was still cold and, at the beginning of this period, very humid. The glaciers had scarcely moved since the days of the Neanderthal man and they still covered the greater part of Northern and Central Europe. Mammoths, reindeer and woolly rhinoceroses lived in more or less numerous herds and are typical of the fauna of the epoch. But they were surrounded by a tundra fauna, especially wild horses, musk oxen, blue foxes, wolverines, cave bears, snow owls, etc. After this first attack of damp cold, a certain amelioration made itself felt and the temperature became more clement. But soon the frost returned, and this time it was very dry and very severe; then to the aforementioned animals were added the bison and the aurochs, together with saiga antelopes, chamois, marmots and some jerboas.

At the beginning of this last act, that is, at the end of the Mousterian and the dawn of the Aurignacian, tribes from North Africa invaded Europe, either by the Straits of Gibraltar or by the straits which separate Malta and Sicily from the African coast. The crossing from Africa to Europe was actually very easy at certain periods of the Reindeer Age, when the straits were very narrow.

The men who thus spread across Europe were men of medium height with long and large heads, large noses, bulging foreheads and receding chins; they were also characterized by the length and narrowness of the pelvis and by the length of their forearms and forelegs as compared with their arms and thighs. They were the negroids of whom two complete skeletons, one an adolescent and the other an old woman, were found in the Italian caves at Grimaldi.

A little later, from the Aurignacian to the Magdalenian, Europe was submerged under an invasion of tribes from the east. These were the Cro-Magnon men, the dolicocephalics (long heads), with short and broad faces. They seemed to come from a region of Asia Minor fairly close to present-day Palestine and they successively invaded Central Europe and Western and Southern Europe, as well as North Africa. During the Reindeer Age new waves of Cro-Magnon men ceaselessly arrived from the east; some of them stopped in Central Europe while others went on until they came to the shores of the Atlantic Ocean and the Mediterranean Sea in Italy and France.

Finally, much later, in the Magdalenian epoch, and probably from Asia once again, came men who constituted the third fossil race of prehistoric times in Western Europe: small men with long heads, but with faces of average size both in length and breadth, very distinctive men with very prominent cheek-bones. These were the Chancelade men. Because it was thought that with the eventual retreat of the ice these Chancelade men moved northwards, and because it was thought that they were therefore the origin of the eastern Eskimos of to-day (those of Labrador and Greenland) whom they strikingly resemble physically, ethnographically and archaeologically—and also because this view has been widespread among the general public and has been supported by very strong arguments—it must be said here that to-day, as a result of the work of Henri Vallois, it is impossible to give continued support to this theory, for Vallois has demonstrated its weakness after very complex anthropological studies.

Thus we have put in their places, in Europe at least, the three great fossil races of *Homo sapiens* in the Reindeer Age. Nevertheless, as regards the origin of these races and also their fate when the Paleolithic Age came to an end, certain survivals are still to be seen in our days and from time to time, in Dordogne for instance, a peasant of great height can be met who is not far removed from the Cro-Magnon type. But it is probably in the Canary Islands that the most eloquent phenomena of survival are to be seen; the natives, whom we call Guanches, are Cro-Magnoids with scarcely any physical or mental change.

*

Then, 10,000 years ago, began the intermediate period called the Mesolithic. The climate continued to grow milder, the glaciers retreated northwards or withdrew into the high mountains, and the first attempts were now made at polishing stone, attempts that were still timid and unskilful, and, moreover, without much future.

It was in the Mesolithic Age that, coming from Eastern Europe, perhaps even from Asia, men of small stature, still dolicocephalic, infiltrated right along the Mediterranean coasts and occupied especially Yugoslavia, Italy, the southern part of France and some parts of Spain. These little long-faced dolicocephalics were very like one of the present-day ethnic types of Europe, the Mediterraneans. On the other hand it was in the Mesolithic Age that round-headed men appeared for the first time in the history of the world, men of small stature who thrust themselves in like a wedge, to set up a comparison, classic in anthropology, between the small dark dolicocephalics of the south and the big fair dolicocephalics of the north of Europe.

Finally, in the Mesolithic Age art and industry were in very definite retreat. Stone implements were mostly of very small size—microliths—of typical shape, like the segments of an orange; they seem to have been used only when fitted to the end of a stick or a bone. Otherwise, the working of bone was very poor and all the awls, harpoons and hooks of stag-horn in this period were rather rough instruments. The only artistic activity of the period seems to have been the coloured pebbles bearing on their surface stripes,

FIG. 57. The implements, like segments of an orange, of the Mesolithic.

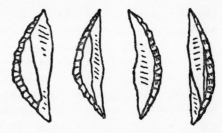

crosses and lines of dots, the significance of which totally escapes us, and although some archaeologists maintain that we should regard them as the rudiments of a written language, we must frankly admit that we cannot read it. Such coloured pebbles have

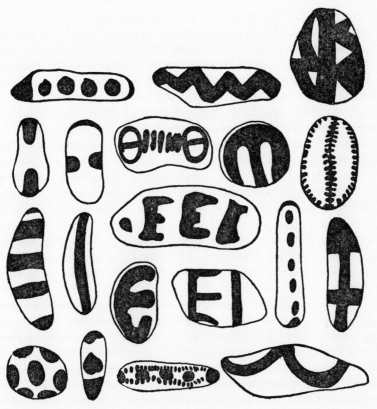

FIG. 58. The enigmatical coloured pebbles from Le Mas d'Azil.

been found in great abundance in the French Pyrenean cave of
Le Mas d'Azil.

At last the age known as the Polished Stone Age, or Neolithic
Age, began. Actually it is in some degree mistaken to use the
term "polished stone" since, as Furon has remarked, although the
polishing technique had at last been brought to perfection, the
manufacture of polished implements was far from being universal
and, in the very great majority of neolithic beds, we always find
an abundance of chipped stones and much rarer polished stones
side by side. On the other hand, what was far more characteristic
of the Polished Stone Age was the economic revolution by which
nomadic man became sedentary, turning from a hunter into a
tiller of the soil.

The milder climate now made life possible in the open air for
the greater part of the year. So, abandoning their dark caves, men
now lived in huts or in dwellings built on piles to form small
villages. A certain organization inevitably appeared, one of the
least questionable signs of which is, for the prehistorian, the organization of funeral ceremonies. This was the epoch in which,
probably due in great part to the mild temperature, three important inventions appeared: the polishing of stone, the domestication of animals and plants, and the making of pottery. But these
three inventions were not everywhere equal. Although, to quote
Furon again, a complete Neolithic was familiar with polished
stone, pottery, the growing of cereals and the domestication of
cattle, sheep, goats and pigs, there were actually very many neolithic tribes who for various reasons knew nothing of one or
the other. In the neighbourhood of Cannes and Nice 5,000 years
ago there lived cultivators and shepherds who had never polished
their stone implements; similarly, there are Australian aborigines
who use chipped stones, but know nothing of pottery or agriculture.

Mme. Pia Zambotti has recently put out a very ingenious theory
to account for the origins of agriculture and pottery. Relying on
our present knowledge of the life and ways of the Franco-Cantabrian hunters, she imagines that in the Reindeer and Mesolithic
Ages, in order to supplement the insufficient supplies of fresh
meat, which must very often have been precarious in the periods
of intense cold, and also in response perhaps to some unconscious
physiological need, vegetable foodstuffs acquired some importance.

It must not be forgotten that certain fossil seeds were found in the caves of the Pekin man, and also in the Paleolithic caves of France and Spain. It is reckoned that the gathering of these vegetables was restricted to the women of the tribe, while the hunters were out, absent perhaps for days in pursuit of the herds of reindeer and bison. In the Reindeer Age men were in contact with animals, and women were in contact with plants. In the desire to speed up the collection of wild berries, the women, according to Mme. Zambotti, were not long in inventing the basket, made of plaited plant matter. Nevertheless, when life in the open was possible, the women responsible for collecting the vegetable food soon observed that it would be much easier to grow certain plants around their villages than to go gathering them after long journeys into the country. It is thus that agriculture may have been invented, at the dawn of the Polished Stone Age, by the females of the nomadic hunting tribes.

Further, in proportion to the development of vegetable foods, the need to carry and to cook the supplies was soon imposed. The first receptacles used for cooking were doubtless the plaited baskets, the interstices being filled with a thin coating of clay; but, as the clay hardened under the action of fire, the plaited lining became useless unless the clay coating was sufficiently thick. Thus was pottery born, but it still kept the memory of its origin in the form of the interlaced marks that the plant stems had originally left in the clay coating. In actual fact, the first articles of pottery were always decorated with regular cross-pieces, made with the finger, which were later transformed into geometrical motifs and then became diversified to the extreme, both in design and colour.

Finally, it is reasonable to try and discover in what regions agriculture and cattle breeding began. To follow Mme. Zambotti to her conclusions, two centres of culture are revealed whence these skills, from which that of pottery cannot be separated, have spread across the world: Mesopotamia (the lands of Sumer and Akkad, between the Tigris and Euphrates) and Egypt. As it is interesting to know the arguments which can be used to support the relationship between the primary centres and the secondary centres of cultivation, the example of the spread of Egyptian agricultural civilization westwards deserves a few comments. This civilization, which was born on the banks of the Nile 9,000 years

ago, spread southwards towards Nubia, and westwards towards
North Africa, whence it reached Europe, oceanic France and then
England, by way of the Straits of Gibraltar. And all along the
African coast of the Mediterranean, across Spain, then along the
Atlantic coast of France, especially in Brittany, as well as in numerous parts of the British Isles, the route of this civilization is
marked by the existence of megalithic monuments, that is to say
menhirs (standing stones), cromlechs or groups of menhirs placed
more or less regularly in circles or lines, dolmens (flat stones lying on standing stones and giving the appearance from a distance
of a table), covered ways (which can be a series of dolmens placed
side by side and forming a tunnel, sometimes partly underground),
etc. These megaliths are now recognized beyond dispute as religious monuments, of striking relationship with Egyptian
tombs.

*

It is impossible here to describe, even briefly, the infinitely
complex mixing of populations that took place in the Neolithic
age. But, because it is a problem which worried anthropologists
for a long time and because the answer was given only a few years
ago, we cannot totally ignore the subject of fossil man in America.

It was in 1951 that the oldest known American was identified
beyond argument. Until then the discoveries of fossil human remains in both North and South America have given rise to epic
disputes. Some stood for the very great antiquity of man in America
and the paleontologist Ameghino, some 30 years ago, even went
so far as to claim for South America in general, and Argentina
in particular, the honour of having been the cradle of humanity.
Others went too far the other way and stood for the thesis of the
late peopling of the Americas. The unfortunately few moderates
took up an intermediate position and reckoned that man appeared in North America about 12,000 to 15,000 years ago, coming from Asia.

But the oldest human relic that has ever been found in America
is a fragment of pelvic bone from a man who lived in North
America 11,000 years ago; it is probably to men of his race that
we must attribute the strange industry of chipped stone called the
Folsom industry, specially characterized by a very flat point, of
which the cutting edges are delicately retouched, while each of the
flat faces shows a wide and deep lengthwise groove.

This discovery is interesting because up till now all the slightly old bones that have been dug up from American soil, whose authenticity is beyond doubt, were always entire skeletons or fragments of skeletons of Indians of modern type; however, the finding of worked stones on the one hand, and on the other hand the existence together in the same bed of human bones and the bones of animals that have now vanished (giant armadillos), indisputably prove that human beings had already penetrated America 10,000 years before our era. The gap is now filled.

Naturally, the human species was already very developed 10,000 years ago (in Western Europe this was the beginning of the Mesolithic Age); also the pelvis that has just been studied in Chicago, and which was found at Natchez in Mississippi, is of almost modern type. It is a fossil race whose type is little different from that of present-day Indians.

*

But a history of life will not be complete if we are content only to present its last phase, that which covers the period from *Parapithecus* to modern man. The origins of man and the origins of life itself must be sought still further back. In the course of this search a stage is clearly marked by a recent discovery which has made a great public stir: that of the Coelacanth, the fossil fish of the Comoro Islands and Madagascar.

Part Two

OUR ANCESTORS THE FISHES

CHAPTER V

The Assault of the Continents

SHORTLY before Christmas in the year 1938 a native fisherman, off the coast of South Africa, was surprised to find in his heavily laden nets a great fish weighing about 110 pounds and measuring about 5 feet in length. Rather puzzled by this strange creature of which he had never seen nor heard the like, he did not at first know if it should be eaten or if it would be better to bring it to the notice of the white man. Fortunately mind triumphed over matter and in the end Miss Latimer, Keeper of the East London Museum, had to shelter the cumbersome creature. Very puzzled by it, too, having never seen this fish before nor any description of it, she decided to ask for help from the capital and wrote to the leading fish expert in South Africa, Professor J. L. B. Smith. The latter expected simply to describe a new species and promised to arrive in East London as soon as the Christmas festivities were over, advising Miss Latimer to preserve the fish meanwhile in the best possible way. Unfortunately, it showed no interest in the Christmas festivities and quietly began to rot. Miss Latimer had to resign herself to gutting it and throwing the entrails away; some days later she called in an expert and asked him to stuff the creature. In the midst of all this Professor Smith reached the museum.

He was lost in amazement; it was almost as if without warning he was suddenly confronted by a living Brontosaur. For the type of fish before which he stood transfixed and of which, lacking the internal organs, he would still be able to study the skeleton, muscles and skin, was well known to the paleontologists. Alive only ten days earlier and now slowly decomposing, this fish was without doubt a Coelacanth, a name which means a fish with fins with hollow spines. These Coelacanths are an order which was thought to have become extinct about 60 million years ago, and belonged to the class with lobbed fins known as the Crossopterygii, which the experts place at the origin of all terrestrial vertebrates.

As a tribute to the patience and initiative of Miss Latimer, Smith described his sensational discovery under the name *Latimeria chalumnae*. Unfortunately, in 1939 the world had other worries: war broke out in Europe shortly after Smith had published his work and the crossopterygian did not receive all the attention it deserved. But Smith himself had only one idea: since the Coelacanths lived between Madagascar and the east coast of Africa, in that part of the Indian Ocean known as the Mozambique Channel, it should be possible to find others, to study them at leisure and perhaps to obtain new ideas about the origin of terrestrial vertebrates. Without respite, he scoured all the country bordering the Mozambique Channel, the coasts of South Africa, Madagascar and the Comoro Islands, warning and questioning the fishermen, and doing some fishing himself. The result was negative.

Some of the natives of the Comoro Islands remembered having on earlier occasions caught fishes that corresponded to the description given by Smith or seen them caught. Otherwise, the creature was extremely rare and for this reason he had to consult the cadi, the religious leader, to find out if there were not some dietary prohibition regarding this uncommon fish, the flesh of which is apparently very fatty and not at all tasty. It is probable that a certain number of Coelacanths had been lost to science to the benefit of Comorian and South African stomachs. The natives did not know.

But for 10 years they knew that Professor Smith was offering 100,000 francs to the first fisherman to bring him a Coelacanth. And the miraculous draught turned up at last in the Comoro Islands, on the east coast of the island of Anjouan, on December 20th, 1952. The deputy administrator had the fish taken to Mutsamudu, the chief place on the island, and it is said that after having telegraphed Madagascar without receiving precise instructions he mentioned the discovery to Captain Hunt of a small English vessel plying regularly between the Comoro Islands and South Africa. The latter had long been warned by Smith of the importance of the Coelacanth and he had taken an active part in the campaign conducted since 1940 to find out the principal characteristics of the fish from the fishermen. So when Hunt saw the fish which had just been taken at Anjouan, he was almost certain that it was the coveted prize. He at once telegraphed Smith, who, filled with impatience, forthwith telephoned Dr. Malan. The latter placed a special airplane at the disposal of the ichthyologist and his wife. But, quickly as he had acted, Smith once again found a 10-day-old fish, somewhat damaged; Hunt had done the best he could to preserve it; he had slashed the fish with a cutlass and had efficiently salted it, which naturally damaged the appearance of the venerable crossopterygian. However, Smith was so moved at the sight of his Coelacanth that he could not refrain from weeping like a child and, watching over it night and day as a box was prepared for taking the precious paleontological trophy to the Cape, he went without eating for 48 hours. And it was thus that the Coelacanth made the return journey in Dr. Malan's plane and well deserved the name *Malania anjouanis*.

But now the affair became a diplomatic incident. In Paris, where he had gone to finish some work, Dr. J. Millot, Professor at the Natural History Museum and Director of the Institute of Scientific Research in Madagascar, was furious that the Coelacanth, caught in French territorial waters, had been carried off by a British scientist. All the French experts held Professor Smith in great esteem, but still. . . ! Taking the initiative this time, Professor Millot, on his return to Madagascar, carried out a campaign amongst the Comorian fishermen. M. Fourmanoir, one of his assistants and an expert on fish and fishing, spent nearly six months in the Comoro Islands, tirelessly describing the fish with the help of photographs to all the fishermen in all the villages, and he too promised the inevitable prize of 100,000 francs. Occasionally, M. Fourmanoir also did some fishing himself, but without success. At Tananarive, Professor Millot had supplies of formaldehyde and insulated zinc-lined cases prepared; these were stored at strategic points of the archipelago. The senior administrator of the Comoro Islands, M. Coudert, put his whole staff on the alert and gave instructions that in the event of a capture Tananarive was to be advised at once and that, while awaiting the arrival of competent persons, the preservation of the "devil," as the Comorians called the Coelacanth, was to be assured. The officer in command of the air force put a plane at the disposal of Professor Millot to go and fetch the Coelacanth as soon as captured.

During the night of the 24th to 25th September, 1953, a fisher-

man from Anjouan, Houmadi Assani, at last brought up on his
deep sea line a superb Coelacanth of 87 pounds, that was 4 feet 3
inches long. The capture took place at 11.30 p.m. Shortly after
midnight, Assani was back at his own port, Mutsamudu, the chief
place on the island. He deposited his precious capture at his home
and rushed to Dr. Garrouste; the latter had often been disturbed
for the sake of some commonplace fish and hesitated a little, but
ended by following the fisherman. When he saw the fish, he went
off to fetch the chief of the sub-division, Lher, who was not yet in
bed. Both were soon on the spot and at once began the injections
and washings with formaldehyde; then at the end of a sleepless
night they enclosed the fish in its zinc-lined case, just in time to
load it on to the regular airplane for Tananarive, which took off
at 6 a.m. So on September 25th, at 1.30 p.m., 14 hours after its
capture, the Coelacanth was unloaded from an Air France Junker
at the capital of Madagascar, where Professor Millot was im-
patiently waiting. He tells as follows the end of the adventure:

"Transferred at once to a truck from the Institute for Scientific
Research, it was taken half-an-hour later into the laboratory prepared for the purpose where, without losing a minute, the examination was energetically begun: weight, various measurements and
photographs succeeded each other, followed by a scrutiny of the
external and internal parasites, the extraction of the viscera, the
removal of pieces of organs for microscopic investigation or of
organic liquids for chemical analysis, and various dissections—
the operators having to be quick to lock themselves up securely
as protection against the crowd of sightseers which had appeared
at once."

Eventually, a fourth Coelacanth was caught at Grande Comore
at the end of January 1954 and a fifth on February 1st. They,
too, went sent to Tananarive in perfect condition and were recently exhibited in Paris. Thanks to the precautions taken by the
Institute for Scientific Research at Madagascar, the three last
Comorian Coelacanths are in perfect condition and France now
possesses the two finest specimens of a fish with lobed fins that a
paleontologist has ever hoped to lay hands on.

The press gave great importance to the Coelacanth, which was
presented as our distant ancestor, our grandfather, our aquatic
pre-Adam at a low stage of evolution, and so on. It is precisely
because the Coelacanth is none of these (at best a small and distant

cousin of man, a little retarded), and also because his existence
raises no less clearly the problem of life's conquest of the continents about 250 million years ago, that it has been so keenly
studied. Although the Coelacanth is not our grandfather, the
grandfather-fish from which all terrestrial vertebrates are derived
must have resembled him a great deal. On the other hand, the
monster from the Comoro Islands which we believed had vanished from the surface of the earth—or rather from the depths
of the waters—at the same time as the *Diplodocus,* the *Iguanodon*
and the pterodactyl, about 80 million years ago, is one of those
puzzling "living fossils," one of those primitive creatures of times
past that are a joy to the paleontologist.

*

Just to look at it, without even giving it close attention, is to
realize that the Coelacanth is not like other fish. All the fins, with

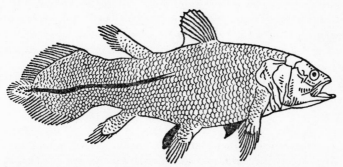

FIG. 59. Coelacanth, showing the fins that have the rudiments
of the feet of terrestrial vertebrates.

the exception of the first dorsal fin, begin with a veritable short
arm carrying long spines joined by a membrane; all other fish,
like those sold every day in all the world's markets, as well as the
rare monsters from the great deeps or from distant oceans, have
fins with spines (or rays, as they are called) that come straight out
of the body, to which they are fixed by a small base plate. Even
more, when the small arm which in the fish with lobed-fins forms
the base of the pectoral fin is dissected, three bones are found, just
as in a human arm, and situated like our humerus, radius and ulna,
prolonged by a multitude of small, short and flat bones comparable to the bones which form a human wrist. The lobed fin of the

crossopterygian is a real fin-foot, which could serve for crawling over the earth; the fins of other fishes are too fragile for that and can serve only for swimming.

But that is not all. On examining the mouth we find at the far end of the palate two long openings by which the nasal cavities connect directly with the throat, known as the choanae (inner nostrils); with their aid the Coelacanth could breathe with its mouth closed, as can all terrestrial vertebrates. For certain "cousins" of this 300-million-year-old fish breathed in an abnormal fashion for a member of the aquatic family, a fashion which is found in practically no present-day fish. Actually, in all terrestrial vertebrates, as in man, the nose has two functions: on the one hand it is the olfactory organ, thanks to the nerve endings in its mucous

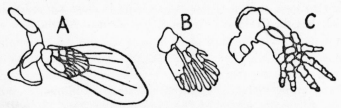

FIG. 60. The three types of foot in vertebrates:
A. The fin of a fish;
B. The fin-foot of Crossopterygii;
C. The foot of a terrestrial vertebrate.

membranes, and on the other hand it is a double passage through which the air passes and, traversing the choanae, reaches the throat, descends the tracheae and ends in the lungs: so the choanae are necessary to the breathing of oxygen in a gaseous state. Contrariwise, fish breathe the oxygen dissolved in the water by means of their gills, which are generally covered by a small protective piece of bone or cartilage; the nostrils are only the external openings of small cavities called the olfactory capsules, a name which fully explains their only function. The Coelacanth has gills as well as the nose of a real terrestrial vertebrate which in other creatures indicates the existence of lungs, which doubtless arise from a transformation of the swim-bladder. So, once again, this fish with lobed fins is nearer to man than all other fishes; it is a fish with fins that are no longer really those of a fish, without being completely the limbs of a terrestrial animal; it is a fish which shows adaptation to a mixed respiration, able to assimilate either the oxygen dissolved in the water or oxygen in a gaseous state. Thus the Coelacanth gives us a picture of aquatic animal life in process of adapting itself to life on dry land.

But that is not all! The stumpy and very rudimentary tail, which is not separated from the body in the least, as in other fish, and the very peculiar cycloid scales, are very primitive characteristics and bear witness to the creature's antiquity.

These features—and many others too technical to dwell on here, notably the anatomical structure of the head—have thus a double significance: they confirm that the Coelacanth is much older than all the terrestrial vertebrates, and also that there is a relationship between the Coelacanth and the terrestrial vertebrates, including man, while the relationship is not very clear, except in the very broad structural lines between the terrestrial vertebrates and the fishes of to-day.

Actually, it was the little black boys of Central Africa who first discovered the evolutive significance of the Coelacanth, many centuries ago without a doubt. For in the region bounded on the north by a line stretching from Senegal to the White Nile, and on the south by the source of the Zambesi and Lake Tanganyika, lives a curious fish able to move on dry land, to make vocal sounds, and to spend about six months out of water, all of which is quite contrary to the normal characteristics of fishes. This creature is a very amusing object for the little black children and it is their habit to go and poke at it with a stick when, during the dry season, it is enclosed in a ball of mud. In these intertropical and equatorial regions torrential rains continue for six months and then the water-courses and small lakes suddenly dry up: when this happens all the aquatic creatures have but one resource, to flee under pain of death. Some of them let themselves be carried along by the current and so reach the larger lakes where life is possible throughout the year. But certain fish have found a neater solution: when there is no water they do without it and secrete a sort of mucus which covers them and keeps them moist for several months; thereafter, they make a kind of nest, a ball of mud with an orifice to which they affix their mouths. It is through these holes that the black children thrust their sticks and tickle the fishes' throats. The fishes protest by blowing out air and emitting a characteristic grunt. This fish is called *Protopterus* and, besides its gills for

breathing oxygen dissolved in the water, has lungs which permit
it to survive the dry season.

The zoologists had to wait until 1870 before they became acquainted with these fishes. They were reported from Australia
and seemed the more precious because, not only did they have
lungs but they appeared to be exceedingly rare, being found only
in two small rivers, the Murray and the Burnett, in Queensland.
Afterwards, other Lung-fish (or Dipnoi, as they are called) were
found in Africa (*Protopterus*) and in South America, in the
Amazon and some of its tributaries (these are called *Lepidosiren*),
where they are by no means rare. These lung-fish provide a very
fine example of an animal's adaptation to its environment, since
with lungs they can lead a double life, in or out of water. This
adaptation exactly explains the methods by which the continents
were conquered.

When we go back 300 million years to the Devonian era, we
find the world populated with very many fishes, especially the
Crossopterygii, like the Coelacanths and the Dipnoi. At that time
an enormous North-Atlantic continent encompassed a great part
of North America, the Atlantic Ocean and Northern Europe. It
is often referred to as the "continent of Old Red Sandstone," because this is the typical geological formation of the Devonian era.
This continent had a tropical climate and experienced the regular
alternation of periods of drought and torrential rain. The landscape was very monotonous, all in vertical lines, dominated by
endless plants resembling our modern horsetail, but 10 feet high
or more, raising their long parallel arms to the sky. In the immense ocean that bounded this continent to the south lived very
many types of fish, all of them very strange, which must be quickly
described if the stages in the conquest of the continents are to be
properly understood.

In the fresh water and in the salt-water lagoons were fairly
numerous and varied species of what are called armoured fish.
Known as Placoderms and Ostracoderms, these fish were covered
with a sort of helmet to protect the head and what for simplicity's
sake may be called the neck and the beginning of the thorax; this
armour, sometimes all of one piece and sometimes of two articulated pieces, was made of a type of bone called "dermal bone,"
because it arose by transformation of certain skin tissue. Laden
with this armour, which often varied in shape, and provided with

superabundant spines, these armoured fishes dragged themselves heavily along close to the bottom of the water-courses and fed on small crustaceans or on other less agile or less well-protected fishes. They themselves were menaced by a kind of large aquatic scorpion known as Eurypterida.

One of the main peculiarities of these armoured fishes was the presence, at the edges of the shield on either side, and also on top of the head, of three lines of small bony plates lightly sunk into the armour. The Swedish scientist Stensiö, who has made a lengthy study of the fossil Ostracoderms of Spitzbergen, regards these formations as electrical organs comparable to those of present-day rays and torpedoes. Stensiö relies upon the anatomical configuration of the nervous system, which he has been able to study in detail, thanks to one peculiarity of the armoured fishes, whereby the principal nerves were enclosed in little ossified conduits. He has thus been able to establish that the three lines of plates were connected by numerous nerves to a certain part of the brain situated behind the olfactory zone. But other paleontologists do not regard this anatomical structure as convincing and believe that the bony lines can equally well be regarded as sense organs permitting the fish to maintain its balance, comparable to the lateral line on either side of the bodies of the majority of modern fishes.

On dry land a few large insects rather like our dragon-flies and a few scorpions were able to maintain themselves after a fashion, for climatic conditions were scarcely favourable. Speaking literally, life had in fact already begun its conquest of the continents, since a few plants and a few invertebrates were to be found there. But really, it was the vertebrates—and they alone—which were to effect a true conquest of the earth, since they would be capable of successfully occupying all the habitable areas and of evolving in infinite variety, so that they would soon be masters of the world and have completed their domination on a planetary scale by the time man made his appearance. But when the Devonian began no vertebrate had yet put fin or foot on dry land. All the vertebrates, which at that time were the fishes of fairly numerous and varied species, lived in the sea and the fresh water. Besides these armoured fishes, dragging themselves along the submarine depths, were Coelacanths of great size which all more or less resembled the Coelacanth of the Comoro Islands. In the fresh waters

were other armoured fish and Dipnoi, too, of which the principal
kind, quite widespread, was *Ceratodus*, very like the present-day
Queensland Dipnoan, for which reason the latter has been called
Neoceratodus.

It was again in the water-courses that the very important fishes
with lobed fins, known as Rhipidistia, developed the habits which,
on the surface of this semi-desert continent of Old Red Sandstone,
with a tropical climate of alternating drought and endless rain,
were comparable to those of the Dipnoi of to-day. Excellent
swimmers, with slender bodies and strong jaws with sharp teeth,
this branch of fishes with lobed fins is true to type in certain
anatomical structures: besides the fins that were carried on small
limbs of the kind already seen in the Coelacanth, and the inner
nostrils (choanae), they had a cranium very like that of present-
day batrachians, showing a certain degree of evolution towards

FIG. 61. One of the best known of Devonian fish: *Osteolepis*.

the terrestrial vertebrate form. These Rhipidistia developed very
quickly and it was from them that the first terrestrial vertebrates,
properly so called, the first amphibia derived.

In their general appearance these first amphibians were still fish
on four feet: they had a long dorsal fin, a flattened tail and short
limbs ending in five fingers. They are called *Ichthyostega* and little
is known of them, since only a few fragmentary bony remains
were discovered in Greenland a few decades ago by a Swedish
expedition under Professor Säve-Soderbergh and by an English
expedition under the paleontologist Westoll. However, in its main
lines it is not impossible to imagine how the conquest of the
continents was affected: when the rainy season ended and the
water-levels began to fall, certain fish with lobed fins and certain
primitive amphibians were able to resist the dry period by making
their way on to dry land and, breathing pure air, making towards
the lakes or water-courses which were not completely dried up,
or by awaiting patiently the return of the wet season. From that

moment life had achieved the conquest of the land, since certain vertebrates were no longer obliged to die when water was lacking. By a strange paradox it is possible to maintain that the fish with lobed fins and the primitive amphibians achieved this conquest simply because they were better adapted than others of their kind to aquatic life: it was just because they were better fitted than the heavy Coelacanths or the Dipnoi which were too specialized to take foot on terra firma in order to go in search of water, that they ended by adapting themselves to life in the air. Other hypotheses have sometimes been suggested to explain this emergence from the water. Since they were carnivorous, the scarcity of prey is one suggestion; but it is a difficult one to maintain, for fish were always very abundant in Devonian seas. The need of these creatures with lungs to come out and breathe pure air has also been suggested, but this could be done very easily by breaking surface, without having to take foot on the shore. In fact, it is because

Fig. 62. One of the first vertebrates to set foot on dry land: *Ichthyostega*.

they were better equipped to endure the climatic conditions of the Devonian that these creatures were able to conquer the continents.

*

Now is the moment to summarize rapidly the principal zoological characteristics that differentiate the terrestrial vertebrates from the aquatic vertebrates.

It is necessary first of all to recall briefly the characteristics of the Crossopterygii, or fish with lobed fins, which must be placed at the origin of all terrestrial vertebrates through the Rhipidistia. These fish had choanae and lungs, and were thus able to breathe pure air; they had fins with bony bases which are comparable to those in the limbs of terrestrial vertebrates; finally, they had a lightened skull and a microscopic dental structure identical to those of the first terrestrial vertebrates.

The Rhipidistia are thus incontestably at the origin of our first amphibians. But between these amphibians (and beyond them all the other terrestrial vertebrates up to and including man) and the fishes are essential differences of which the principal are as follows. Fishes live in a dense medium and the Archimedean pressure they receive as a result of the weight of the water they displace supports them in their medium, so that one can say that the problem of gravity does not arise in practice. It is exactly the reverse for the terrestrial vertebrates, whose bodies have to resist a very considerable pressure which tends to flatten them to the earth. So in terrestrial vertebrates one sees the limbs strengthened and lengthened: these are the three bones in the fins of the Crossopterygii, homologous to the humerus, radius and ulna, which are at the origin of the general structure of the limbs of terrestrial vertebrates. On the other hand, fishes breathe the oxygen dissolved in the water through their gills, while terrestrial vertebrates breathe gaseous oxygen through their lungs, which involves the existence of inner nostrils and a more or less complex respiratory passage.

Fishes, because they live always in the water, are not subject to desiccation, while in the atmosphere evaporation is continuous: vertebrates have to resist evaporation of the liquids of the system by various mechanisms, such as the thickening of the skin and the appearance of a protective covering of scales, hair, feathers, and so on. Finally, another essential difference between fishes and terrestrial vertebrates concerns the locomotor system: it is by undulations of the body and tail that a fish moves through the water and, contrary to what is often thought, the fins are above all the organs which assure balance and prevent the fish from rolling on its side. Contrariwise, in terrestrial vertebrates it is the limbs, which are directly derived from fins, which are the essential organs of locomotion, while the tail becomes simply an organ of balance, counterbalancing the weight of the head, short of losing all functional utility and even disappearing.

The Coelacanths of the Mozambique Channel and the Dipnoi of Central Africa, the Australian deserts and the Amazon have already achieved the essential requirement of terrestrial life. But, in full conformity to the laws of evolution, the Coelacanths as well as the Dipnoi are only living fossils, retarded creatures which survive to-day as evidence of the existence of a certain stage of

Aurignacian polychrome painting on the ceiling of one of the caverns
at Lascaux. (Dordogne.)

Armoured fish (Ostracoderms) of the Devonian period, contemporary
with the Coelacanth. (Piveteau: *Images des mondes disparus.*)

COMPARISON BETWEEN FISH AND CHOANICHTHYES

FISH	CHOANICHTHYES
Nostrils opening into olfactory cavities without outlet	Nasal cavities connecting with the throat through inner nostrils
Respiration of dissolved oxygen	Respiration of gaseous oxygen
Gills	Lungs
Fins	Limbs with five bony rays, ending in five fingers

evolution through which life has passed, but they in no event gave rise to terrestrial vertebrates. And for this there is an excellent explanation: if the Coelacanths and Dipnoi had been on the direct line of evolution to the terrestrial vertebrates we would not have the pleasure of making their acquaintance to-day, except as fossils. If we should one day, for example, find "the abominable snowman" in the Himalayas and discover that he is half ape and half man, we shall not have laid hands on our ancestor, but will simply have found the proof of a certain evolutionary stage through which the ancestors of man have passed: like this hypothetical snowman, the Coelacanths and Dipnoi are only the "failures" of evolution, they are the ends of evolutionary series which have continued until our day without transformation for 200 million years. Thus the Coelacanth from the Comoro Islands, though interesting to the zoologist and paleontologist, cannot in any way be regarded as our "grandfather," but at best a first cousin once removed.

*

Therefore, something like 275 million years ago, at the end of the Devonian and the beginning of the Carboniferous, the first true amphibians appeared, called labyrinthodonts because the internal structure of their teeth, like those of the fish with lobed fins, had the appearance of a labyrinth. The first of these amphibians, those of the Carboniferous, had limbs that were still quite weak and they led a life that was almost wholly aquatic. On the other hand, in the Permian, some 220 million years ago, there appeared amphibians of great size, with very strong limbs, that led a terrestrial life. The best known of these was a sort of enormous crocodile, heavy, strong and thick-set, its dental structure indi-

cating that it was undoubtedly a formidable carnivore; this was
the Texan *Eryops*. Later still, in the Trias, 190 to 150 million
years ago, the amphibians returned to an aquatic life, with forms
of great size, but with long and flattened bodies, and with very
weak limbs. Then, at the end of the Trias, came the most important
forms of our present-day amphibians, the Anura (toads and frogs),
which are derived from labyrinthodonts of small size; it was from
other amphibian forms that the Urodeles are derived (salamanders
and newts), but the paleontological studies that have been resumed in recent years no longer allow us to make the Dipnoi derive
from them as was once thought. Thus, from the middle of the
Secondary era, when the first giant reptiles began to dominate

FIG. 63. A primitive vertebrate: *Eryops*.

the world, the main types of our present amphibians, very modest
both in size and number, were already fixed.

But it must not be forgotten that it was through an amphibian
stage that life passed on to complete the conquest of the
continents.

However, the amphibians were not yet equipped to bring this
conquest to success and finally to exploit it, for, although they
effected the necessary anatomical adaptations, they had not acquired that indispensable perfection which concerns the method
of reproduction. It can be said that the amphibians have kept a
memento, even a bad memento, of their fish ancestors: they remain tied to the water for reproductive purposes. It is in the
water that their eggs must be laid, it is in the water that they have
to hatch, and it is in the water that the first larval forms must
develop—the tadpoles—which are provided only with gills and
only acquire lungs at the critical moment of their metamorphosis.
It is the reptilian stage of the terrestrial vertebrates that definitely

threw off that servitude to water; at this stage appeared the fundamental improvement in the mode of reproduction which is the
incubation of the young inside a shell egg. And this is the place,
still in the ascent to man, to sketch the astonishing domination of
the Secondary world by the giant reptiles.

CHAPTER VI

In the Days of the Reptiles

THE curtain rises on a tropical landscape, though the scene corresponds to the modern American state of Wyoming in the Rocky Mountains, almost at the spot where the Colorado now has its source. But there are no mountains yet; at most, a few hills stand out here and there from an immense, swampy and sombre expanse. Plants of great size, some rooted in the shallows of the swamps and others definitely terrestrial, in most of these places form a protective screen through which the sun's rays find difficulty in passing. Tree-ferns and gigantic conifers mingle with giant horsetails. The heat is suffocating and the air, supersaturated with water vapour, is almost unbreathable, for it is difficult for the winds to stir through the exuberant vault of vegetation.

Elsewhere the dense tropical forest opens up a little; a watercourse winds its way along and empties into a deep swamp from which spring a few aquatic plants of striking greenness. And further off is the sea, a sea of over-warm water, perpetually heated by the implacable rays of the eternal sun.

Suddenly the scene wakes up. From the water emerges a flattened head with small eyes standing out from the level of the skin; a head borne upon a neck 7 or 8 yards long. A scaly back, quite as long, breaks the surface. The *Brontosaurus* slowly, lazily turns its head; a little further away another *Brontosaurus* soon appears, and then another. On seeing these heavy aquatic creatures, one cannot refain from thinking of the herds of hippopotamuses to-day. But that is far from correct, for although the hippopotamus of two tons can seem of considerable size, *Brontosaurus*, with its 40 tons and a length of 25 yards, beats it hollow.

Suddenly the creature is on the alert. Clearing a way for itself through a mass of ferns, standing up on its hind feet, which apart from their size cannot be better compared than with those of a chicken, with long, strong, clawed toes, an *Allosaurus*, covered with large scales, moves forward. With its body leaning forwards, carrying its head some 10 to 12 feet above the earth, its huge mouth, stretching to behind the eyes and showing many pointed teeth, its long tail waving to secure balance, and its ridiculously short fore-feet pressed to its body, the *Allosaurus* soon reaches the swamp and hurls itself upon the nearest *Brontosaurus*. Despite its apparent strength, the latter is vanquished at once. How can it escape effectively, even if all it has to do is submerge, since it has a neck and tail of such inordinate length, offering a prize to the attacker at the least movement? How can it escape since it weighs 40 tons, and cannot even react effectively in the torpor engendered by this heavy humid heat, having only a minute and rudimentary brain?

*

Elsewhere, in other parts of this Jurassic landscape, 150 million years ago, similar scenes were enacted. In the shadow of huge plants gigantic reptiles struggled for life. For more than 100 million years the earth, peopled with giant animal and vegetable forms, was a world seen through the magnifying glass. On the lines of *Brontosaurus* (a massive body supported by four short thick limbs, the fore-limbs being a little shorter than the hind-limbs, a large tail, and a large neck ending in a little head) was a whole

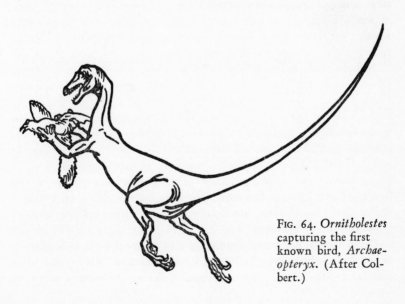

FIG. 64. *Ornitholestes* capturing the first known bird, *Archae-opteryx*. (After Colbert.)

series of aquatic herbivores: *Diplodocus*, 20 yards long, with nostrils at the top of its head, just in front of the eyes, *Camarasaurus, Cetiosaurus*, etc. Elsewhere, in the swamps which covered the greater part of East Africa and Europe, were the *Atlantosaurus*, a giant among giants with a length of 40 yards, and the *Brachiosaurus* which, as an exception, had fore-legs longer than the hind-legs, which gave it a sharply sloping back-line like a giraffe's, which it otherwise resembles in general appearance, with its very long neck and relatively short tail.

All these huge creatures were aquatic herbivores. On the model of the terrestrial carnivores (*Allosaurus*) were the *Megalosaurus* and, of a notably smaller size (5 to 6 feet, including the tail), the very agile *Ornitholestes*.

However, other herbivores were better armed to face the carnivores than *Diplodocus* and its cousins of the marshes. *Stegosaurus*, also terrestrial, was one of the most curious animals of the Wyoming fauna. A quadruped about 8 yards long, with fore-limbs half the length of its hind-limbs, it moved with its back sharply arched, raised to the level of its haunches and sloping down fairly steeply to end in a long flat tail. Like the hedgehog, the *Stegosaurus* practised passive defence; it was capable when occasion demanded of rolling itself up and presenting its adversary with a hard armour, while along its back was a double line of large triangular bony plates; but it could also defend itself actively with very formidable blows from a powerful tail that ended in four sharp spikes. Imagine the difficulty a carnivore would find when faced with this well-protected creature, larger than an elephant!

*

A little further off, in seas that are filled with coral reefs, or on their shores, are other equally strange creatures, like *Rhamphorhynchus*, a caricature of a bat: a little smaller than a pigeon, it perches at the top of a cliff with wings outstretched; it springs into the air, hovers, maintains itself with a few wing-beats, soars, descends, makes a turn or two, profiting by the rising currents of warm air above the sea, and finally, having caught its prey during flight, comes to rest on the beach.

On this beach marine crocodiles sun themselves before setting off to hunt; with long bodies and long muzzles, with paddle-like feet and tails flattened like rudders, these Jurassic crocodiles,

Geosaurus and *Metriorhynchus,* are remarkably adapted for under-water hunting.

Exclusively aquatic and mercilessly carnivorous, the giant reptiles still dominate the marine sphere in the shape of *Plesiosaurus* and *Ichthyosaurus. Ichthyosaurus* gives the impression that it is a fish because of its general shark-like appearance; it has a stream-lined body and limbs that are truly fins, a long and narrow snout filled with many pointed teeth, and a forked tail, which is asymmetrical and has two unequal lobes, the upper one large and rounded and the lower one narrow and pointed. Moreover, in a wholly fish-like manner it moves rapidly by lateral undulation of the body, amplified by a vigorous thrust from the tail, the lateral fins allowing the creature to turn and to stop and assuring stability of the body after the manner of a balancer.

Plesiosaurus, on the contrary, has a large flat body, its intermina-

FIG. 65. *Mesosaurus,* marine reptile of the Cretaceous.

ble tail and neck making it look like a turtle with a long serpent passing right through it. Its four short limbs are like paddles and serve to propel it along, the tail playing the part of a rudder. Thrusting its strong carnivorous jaws in every direction, it captures the fish which are its food.

*

We shall pass over some tens of millions of years and bring our attention to a landscape of the Cretaceous, 75 million years more recent than the Jurassic, just described. Few changes have actually taken place.

The climate is certainly milder, more bearable; or rather, there now exist three clearly divided climatic zones; an equatorial zone, hot and humid, stretching round the globe like a belt and separating two relatively temperate zones to north and south.

On the whole, the same reptilian types as in the Jurassic are still to be found. There are giant carnivores like *Tyrannosaurus*, the largest ever of all the carnivores, more than 50 feet long and weighing about 10 tons, and able to raise its head something like 20 feet above the ground. It is rather like an enlarged *Allosaurus*. Somewhat smaller than this creature, but constructed on the same lines, are *Gorgosaurus* and *Ceratosaurus*, which is distinguished by the horn on top of its nose.

The giant herbivores, *Diplodocus*, *Brontosaurus*, etc., have vanished, but other herbivores, no less curious though smaller, almost take their place. These are *Iguanodon* and the duck-billed dinosaur. Very alike in their general appearance these animals sometimes

FIG. 66. *Tyrannosaurus*, one of the most formidable of Cretaceous carnivores.

move on their hind feet only and sometimes on all four. They lead a semi-aquatic life, scarcely moving far from the swamps which provide them with an abundance of green plant life. They have very stout down-turned beaks, very effective for biting and tearing off the leaves, while powerful molars, situated at the back of the mouth complete the mastication. Their webbed feet even permit them to venture into a liquid environment. The series of duck-billed dinosaurs is distinguished by the exuberant bony crests which decorate their noses or skulls.

Corresponding to the strongly armoured *Stegosaurus* is the *Ankylosaurus*, entirely covered with strong bony plates like our modern armadillos, and possessing a formidable weapon in its heavy stubby tail. Beside it are new forms remarkably equipped for defence: the horned dinosaurs, the most representative of which is *Triceratops*. Thirty feet long, it has an enormous head, representing more than a third of its body length and ending in a vast collar covering its neck and shoulders; on the parrot-beak muzzle are one short horn above the nose and two others above the eyes. All the cousins of the *Stegosaurus* also have horns and a vast collar which make them resemble more or less a modern rhinoceros.

Flying reptiles are represented by *Pteranodon* which often

FIG. 67. *Triceratops*, a reptile of the Cretaceous.

confines itself to hovering, keeping itself in the air by slight wing-movements and making best use of the ascending currents of warm air. On the fresh-water shores, as at the edge of the sea, our modern crocodiles are already in existence; the giant type, the *Phobosuchus*, 50 feet long, has now vanished. The seas themselves are the domain of enormous water-lizards, 20 feet long or more, their bodies ending in very long tails; they move with the aid of short, paddle-like limbs. These are *Mososaurus* and *Tylosaurus*.

*

One of the first discoveries of the giant reptiles of the Secondary era to be identified with any precision was probably *Mososaurus*, found in 1780 in a gravel-pit at Pietersberg, near Maestricht in Holland. It at once attracted the attention of the quarrymen and work was suspended to give Dr. Hofmann, a French military surgeon, the time to hurry to the site where he had earlier discovered some fossils that were worthy of interest. The skill of this amateur paleontologist has enabled us to possess the fossil intact: the 16-foot skeleton was inbedded in a block of stone and was extracted from the quarry unbroken. But a Dutchman then intervened: Dr. Goddin, Dean of the Cathedral Chapter. As proprietor of the land above the quarry, he claimed the fossil as his personal property; Hofmann had not only to hand his *Mososaurus* over to Goddin but was charged with costs by the court to which Goddin appealed.

In 1794 the French armies invaded Holland and laid siege to Maestricht, which was cruelly bombarded, with the exception of the suburb where Dr. Goddin had sheltered his *Mososaurus*. Thinking that such clemency could have only one object—the triumphant reconquest of the *Mososaurus*—Goddin took precautions and hid the fossil in a nearby cave. It required nothing less than the promise of 600 bottles of wine for a group of French grenadiers, after searching the country for several days, to return with *Mososaurus;* it was at once sent to Paris, where it can still be admired.

The history of the discovery of the reptiles of the Secondary continued in the admirable finds of an Englishwoman, Mary Anning. At the beginning of the nineteenth century the shores of the English south coast were reputed for sea odours that were regarded as especially invigorating. Here was established a souvenir seller, Richard Anning, whose specialty consisted in selling "old shells" to the visitors, fossil shells found in the chalk and dating from the Secondary. His daughter Mary helped him in this hunt for souvenirs, and in 1811, when she was 12 years old, she discovered the skeleton of *Ichthyosaurus*. Ten years later she provided the scientific world with the first skeleton of *Plesiosaurus*, and in 1828 that of the first flying reptile found in England, not to mention the many other skeletons of *Ichthyosaurus* discovered in the meantime.

It was in 1822, also in England, that the wife of Dr. Gideon Mantell, a doctor interested in paleontology, discovered some strangely shaped teeth in Sussex. They were sent for proper identification to the eminent geologist, Charles Lyell, who in turn sought the advice of Baron Georges Cuvier, who after 1798 was the great authority on paleontological matters. After mature consideration, Cuvier declared they were the teeth of a rhinoceros. But, unsatisfied with the diagnosis, Dr. Mantell returned to the quarry and had the good fortune to extract a few bones. Once more solicited by Lyell, Cuvier this time declared that it was a hippopotamus. After this Mantell resumed the study of the teeth and bones he had discovered and saw that he was faced with a new type of reptile of great size, its teeth being somewhat like those of modern iguanas; hence the name *Iguanodon*. Mantell and other paleontologists at first regarded *Iguanodon* as a quadruped, and it took nothing less than the discovery in a Belgian coal-mine at the end of the last century of 17 skeletons of *Iguanodon* to restore its bipedalism to this animal; in the process it became one of the best known of the dinosaurs. These 17 skeletons, raised eventually on their hind-legs, to-day welcome the visitor to the Natural History Museum at Brussels, and the effect is truly striking.

During the nineteenth century the hunt for dinosaurs was pursued with the greatest energy in the plains and mountains of the western United States, thanks to the scientific rivalry of two eminent American paleontologists, Edward Cope and Othniel March, each with but one desire, to discover one dinosaur more than the other. More recently, further discoveries have been made in Russia, Mongolia and South Africa.

*

But it is now time to take a general view of the reptile group in order to study the various lines and to emphasize at the same time the evolutive importance of this stage in the history of life, a stage which is in the long run that of the conquest of the dry land by living creatures.

Actually it was at the end of the Primary—say 250 million years ago—that the problem of life in the air was solved: from that moment vertebrates were able to live on the earth's surface, were even able to adapt themselves to life in the air without being forced to return to the water in order to reproduce. This final adaptation resulted from the new method of reproduction acquired by the reptiles: the shell egg. The wonderful flight of the birds, the spread of the mammals, and man's conquest of the earth, have all been made possible by this marvellous achievement.

The essential—fundamental—difference, in so far as the history of life is concerned, between the amphibians and the reptiles is in their method of reproduction. This biological phenomenon cannot be over-emphasized. Amphibians, either past or present, always have to return to the water to lay their eggs and to spend the first stage of their lives there as larvae, which are generally known as tadpoles. To reproduce themselves, amphibians are therefore obliged to find lakes, pools, swamps and streams in the region where they live. Reptiles, on the contrary, by reproducing themselves through the intermediary of eggs with shells, have acquired the ability to reproduce wherever they may be, no longer having to take into account the proximity of any water whatever.

It is the shell egg that constitutes the great revolution in the history of life at this reptilian stage through which all the vertebrates have passed; the shell egg, within which the embryo is enclosed in a double protective envelope, the calcareous shell being lined on its inner face with a membrane called the amnion (or

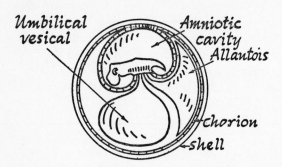

Fig. 68. A vital reptile "invention": the shell egg.

chorion). In this, through the pores in the calcareous shell, the embryo gets its oxygen by means of a respiratory membrane, the allantois. Thanks to this new method of reproduction, the reptiles set out to the conquest of the world and to occupy the most diverse regions, advancing to the heart of the continents without fear of the torrid heat of the deserts, since they no longer needed water for reproductive reasons.

The first conquest of the dry land was thus effected by the reptiles. It began at the end of the Primary and found its apogee during the Secondary, during the 120 million years which separate the beginning of the Triassic from the end of the Cretaceous.

This conquest of the continents is in itself an important fact in the history of life, but it is not all. In fact the birds and the mammals directly descend from the primitive reptiles, so that the reptiles take on a very great importance from the fact that the most developed animals on our planet to-day have all passed through a reptile stage, have all known their "reptile hour."

*

It is essential first of all to search for the origin of the reptiles, for what was the first creature on the surface of the earth to begin to lay eggs with shells. This first animal is called *Seymouria*, because it was found in the environs of a town in Texas called Seymour. Like the amphibians, this first reptile, despite its lizard-like look, had a powerful body, a massive skull of thick bone, and limbs springing horizontally from the body, just like our modern lizards. In fact, it is difficult to know if this animal, possessing the

FIG. 69. *Seymouria*, one of the first animals to lay shell eggs.

majority of the features of its ancestors and contemporaries, the labyrinthodonts, is still an amphibian or already a reptile. However that may be *Seymouria*, prototype of the order of Cotylosauria, must be regarded as the direct ancestor of the giant reptiles, the mammals and the birds.

Then life, having reached the vertebrate stage independent of the water, blazed up fiercely. In a few million years the earth was peopled with gigantic creatures whose names, from *Diplodocus* to *Iguanodon, Brontosaurus* and pterodactyl, are in all the textbooks. Furthermore, reptilian life, not content with having finally achieved the capacity to live without anxiety on terra firma, launched its armies by land, sea and air to effect the conquest of the whole world.

From the cotylosaurian ancestor several evolutive lines branched off, which we must follow one after the other from the Triassic to

the Cretaceous in order to know the principal personages of the
landscape in the Secondary.

On the one hand, by way of reptiles of small size, the thecodonts,
the lines of the giant dinosaurs, crocodiles, flying reptiles and birds
were to split off; while on the other hand, also stemming from
the Cotylosauria, the lines of the turtles and mammals and two
lines of aquatic reptiles (*Plesiosaurus* and *Ichthyosaurus*) were to
appear.

All these evolutionary branches of the reptile class should not
lead us to forget their common features:

reproduction by shell egg;

a variable internal temperature; [1]

respiration of air by means of lungs;

scale-covered skins;

differentiation of the vertebral column into clearly demarcated
    regions (cervical, dorsal, lumbar, sacral and caudal) ;

the position of the limbs, characterized by their parallel direc-
    tion to the body;

the appearance, behind the eyes, of one or two temporal fossae
    in the cranial bone. This "fenestration" of the cranium helps
    to lighten it.

Only the turtles and a few reptiles of lesser importance do not
show all these features.

*

The thecodonts, the main group from which many reptiles
were derived, were bipeds. For the first time in the history of life
vertebrates stood up on their hind-feet and only used their fore-
feet for gripping or for defence. This bipedalism is an important
phenomenon, and much later in the history of life it was to receive
its final expression with the appearance of man. Yet for the
reptiles of the Secondary it already involved a certain number of
important modifications to the skeleton and muscular system; the
hind-limbs became long and strong, making rapid movement
possible, while the fore-limbs became relatively short and slender
and ended in a sort of hand. Another important consequence was

---

[1] That is to say, rising by a few degrees above the surrounding temperature. The
term cold-blooded vertebrates, used in respect of the reptiles as well as fishes and amphibians, is incorrect: it is a matter of animals with a variable temperature, or poecilothermal, as distinct from animals with a constant inner temperature, or homeothermal
—mammals and birds, generally known as warm-blooded vertebrates.

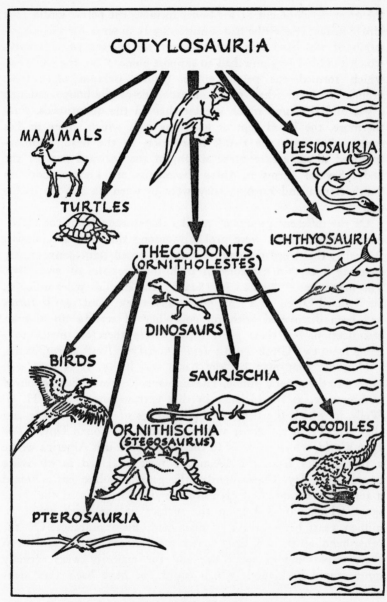

The Principal Lines of the Secondary Reptiles, etc.

the great development of the bones forming the pelvic girdle (the hips) ; in fact this girdle had simultaneously to serve for the articulation of the hind legs and to carry the weight of the body, which the hind legs now had to support alone. Also, the six bones which formed the pelvic girdle (ilium, ischium and pubis, grouped to form a half-girdle on each side of the body) assumed a size and thickness much greater than in the quadrupeds. Furthermore, the biped reptiles had long tails which, more or less symmetrical with the trunk in relation to the head, counterbalanced to some extent the weight of the forward part of the body. Several forms of these thecodonts are known, both in South Africa and Europe; they were between 20 and 40 inches tall.

Of the different groups of reptiles that sprang from the thecodonts, the dinosaurs were probably among the most spectacular. Actually, this word dinosaur is a rather broad term conveniently covering a certain category of prehistoric reptiles of great size. The name was originated in 1842 by the English paleontologist, Sir Richard Owen, at a time when only a few giant reptile forms had been discovered with no possibility of setting up a strict classification. For these giant forms Owen therefore made up a name from two Greek words: *deinos,* terrifying, and *sauros,* lizard.

However that may be, the name was lucky. It is now well known to the general public. The dinosaurs have also been honoured in literature, as for instance in that extravagant tale by H. G. Wells, in which the hero obtains the eggs of a giant reptile and they soon begin to hatch; and in the book by Conan Doyle, *The Lost World,* which takes us to the forests of South America where a few reptiles from the Secondary were imagined as surviving to our own day. Consequently, the general public has acquired a few false notions. No prehistoric man had ever seen the dinosaurs, which vanished from the surface of the earth about 70 million years before the first man made his appearance. On the other hand, all the dinosaurs were not formidable giant carnivores; there were some of small size and the majority were actually quite stupid herbivores, which could not have been very dangerous.

It was in the Jurassic, 160 million years ago, that the first true dinosaurs differentiated themselves from the small biped reptiles, the thecodonts. The general evolutive tendencies within the dino-

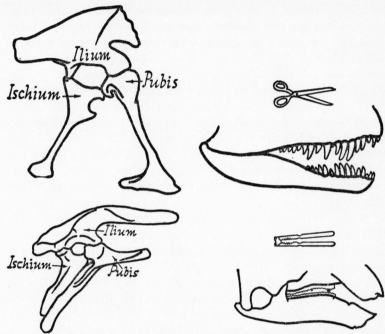

FIG. 70. *Above:* the reptile pelvis and scissor-like jaws of
Saurischia. *Below:* the bird-like pelvis and nut-cracker-like
jaws of Ornithischia.

saur group were gigantism on the one hand and bipedalism on
the other. But at first the dinosaurs split up in the two following
ways, forming two distinct orders, which is why the word dinosaur,
used for both, has no precise zoological meaning. It is easy to
enter this or that dinosaur in one or the other of the two orders,
on the basis of its pelvic form and the articulation of its
jaws.

Some dinosaurs had a pelvis constructed like that of a modern
bird: the ilium and ischium were relatively narrow and long, and
the pubis, also narrow and long, stretched backwards in a bony
projection known as the post-pubis, parallel to the ischium. This
order therefore bears the name Ornithischia (from the Greek
words for bird and hips) or Avipelvians (from the Latin words).
The jaws functioned like a pair of nutcrackers.

The other order of dinosaurs was distinguished by a pelvis

analogous to that of modern reptiles; ilium, ischium and pubis were relatively squat and the pubis had no bony prolongation. The jaws functioned like a pair of scissors. This was the order of Saurischia or Sauripelvians (names derived respectively from the Greek or Latin terms for lizard and hips).

These two orders began to appear in the Jurassic in two biped forms; later came the quadruped forms. Furthermore, the animals of both orders were at first of modest size, then they showed a clear and increasing tendency to gigantism as their evolution proceeded.

*

Saurischia included biped carnivorous forms with sharp dagger-

FIG. 71. An ostrich without feathers: the reptile *Struthiomimus*.

shaped teeth, and quadruped herbivorous forms with teeth generally flattened for grinding. Among the carnivorous bipeds (or theropods) were *Ornitholestes* and *Allosaurus* of the Jurassic, and *Tyrannosaurus, Gorgosaurus* and *Ceratosaurus* (with horned nose) of the Cretaceous. A single exception should be noted: one of the theropods was not carnivorous, but herbivorous; this creature, with the general appearance of an ostrich without feathers— whence its name *Struthiomimus*—had a long neck and a toothless beak.

Among the herbivorous quadrupeds, or souropods, were the famous giant dinosaurs, so well-known to the public. With the exception of a few whales, these are the largest and heaviest animals that have ever lived on the surface of the earth. Their

general appearance was still that of *Diplodocus*, with a massive body
supported on four short and pillar-like limbs, a long tail and a long
neck ending in a small head. However, despite their robust appearance, the legs seem to have been too weak to support the
weight of several tens of tons on dry land: the herbivorous giants
were only able to live in the water, and if they risked themselves
outside their liquid element, they would inevitably have collapsed
under their own weight. Moreover, other arguments militate in
favour of this aquatic habitat: in the majority of them—and this
is especially clear with *Diplodocus* and *Brachiosaurus*—the nostrils
and eyes were situated on the upper part of the head, as with the
hippopotamus and the majority of aquatic animals of to-day, thus
permitting the animal to breathe and to look around without
raising its body or head out of the water, that is to say, by attract-
ing the minimum of attention from a possible enemy. Moreover, the remains of these sauropods are to-day found in the
geological deposits corresponding to ancient rivers or marshes. All
these forms—*Plateosaurus, Brontosaurus, Diplodocus, Camarasaurus, Cetiosaurus, Brachiosaurus*, etc.—are from the Jurassic age.

*

The order Ornithischia also includes biped forms (*Iguanodon*
and the duck-billed dinosaurs) and quadruped forms (*Stegosaurus*
and horned dinosaurs).

The former lived very probably at the edges of lakes, swamps
and rivers, feeding upon leaves from the trees and aquatic grasses,
which they tore with jaws shaped like horned beaks and afterwards crushed with their innumerable grinding teeth at the back
of the mouth.

The duck-billed dinosaurs, or trachodonts, resembled ducks not
only in their beaks—flat, toothless, and covered with a horny
sheath—but also in their webbed feet; they had to spend much
of their lives in the water and in turning over the mud in search of
food, just as do the palmipeds of to-day. Only in size does the
comparison fail. Otherwise, these trachodonts are almost all distinguished by bony excrescences on the nose that rise above the
beak or behind the head. With *Kritosaurus* the thickening of the
bones formed simply a beaked nose; *Corythosaurus* had a flattened
vertical crest resembling that of the modern cassowary; *Lambeosaurus* had a double crest, one part flattened and the other raised

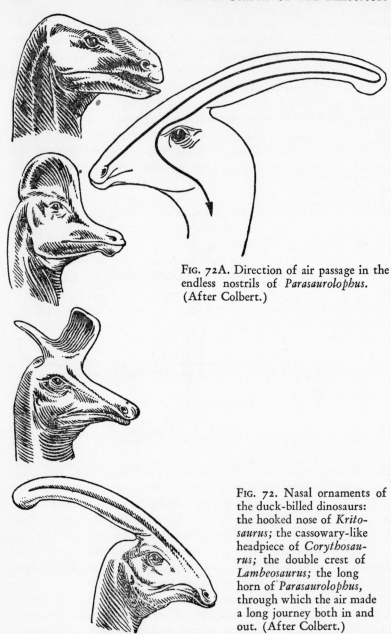

FIG. 72A. Direction of air passage in the endless nostrils of *Parasaurolophus*. (After Colbert.)

FIG. 72. Nasal ornaments of the duck-billed dinosaurs: the hooked nose of *Kritosaurus*; the cassowary-like headpiece of *Corythosaurus*; the double crest of *Lambeosaurus*; the long horn of *Parasaurolophus*, through which the air made a long journey both in and out. (After Colbert.)

above the eyes like an axe-blade, with a backward-sloping point; finally, *Parasaurolophus* was distinguished by a long and narrow horn-shaped crest pointing backwards. These crests have been dissected: inside was found an enlarged nasal passage, forming an air chamber, a supplementary feature demonstrating the adaptation of these animals to the aquatic life, permitting them to remain under water for a long time without rising to breathe. In brief, the trachodonts show their adaptation to an aquatic life by their webbed feet, by the anatomy of their primary respiratory passages and by their flat and narrow tails, all of which lead one to think

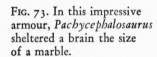
FIG. 73. In this impressive armour, *Pachycephalosaurus* sheltered a brain the size of a marble.

that these animals could live like seals, swimming with some skill and in certain circumstances coming to rest on dry land.

Other trachodonts were devoid of excrescences, but the bone of the skull was thickened in an abnormal way, forming a dome to protect the brain, while the part of the face in front of the eyes and the back of the head were covered with nodules, spikes and spines. The strangest-looking was *Pachycephalosaurus,* with a skull about 10 inches thick, enclosing a minute brain.

Beside the biped Ornithischia were quadruped Ornithischia, which all show this common characteristic of being protected either by a carapace (*Stegosaurus* and *Ankylosaurus*), or by powerful horns, a little like the present-day rhinoceros (horned dinosaurs

FIG. 74. Formidable in appearance, but probably a quite peaceful herbivore: *Stegosaurus* of the Jurassic.

or *Ceratopsia*). Like the Ornithischia just described, their jaws ended in a horned beak: all these animals were herbivorous.

The Jurassic *Stegosaurus*, already described, was typical in the double series of triangular plates on its back and its strong tail ending in four long spines. But apart from its strange appearance, *Stegosaurus* owes its fame to the small size of its brain; an animal of the size of an elephant but with cerebral hemispheres not exceeding the volume of a nut! The spinal cord, on the other hand, shows a swelling at the level of the lumbar vertebrae which is 20 times larger than the brain: this lumbar swelling controlled the movements of the hind-limbs and the tail, which was truly a powerful weapon of defence.

To *Stegosaurus* in the Jurassic corresponded the *Ankylosaurus* in

FIG. 75. The three brains of *Stegosaurus*:
A. Lumbar swelling on the spinal cord;
B. Cervical swelling;
C. Encephalus.

FIG. 76. *Ankylosaurus:*
the most heavily
armoured of the
Cretaceous reptiles.

the Cretaceous, with plates formed of a bony sheet lined with a sheet of horn overlapping one another over the whole body surface from the head to the tail, as with armadillos, forming a protective armour.

The last of the dinosaurs to appear on the earth, where they only had a short stay of a few million years, were the Ceratopsia, or horned dinosaurs, forming the last group of Ornithischia. The oldest of them, called *Psittacosaurus* because of the shape of its upper jaw, which ended in a hooked bill like that of a parrot, was found in Mongolia. It was there, too, that were discovered the remains of *Protoceratops*, of which we possess a fairly large number of skeletons, especially skulls, showing the various phases of its development. Several nests of this animal have also been discovered, including eggs almost the size of turkey eggs; inside two of them we have been able to isolate small embryos on the point of hatching.

All the horned dinosaurs had a bony collar to protect the neck and shoulders; it was a prolongation of the skull and was typical of the family. The many fossils of the Mongolian *Protoceratops* have shown that the bony collar was non-existent in the young when they left the egg and that it developed progressively as they grew up. In addition, the final forms of this group which lived at

FIG. 77. *Protoceratops:*
several of its egg-
filled nests have been
found in Mongolia.

the end of the Cretaceous had horns that were more or less numerous and developed.

It is interesting, in concluding this rapid review of the various types of dinosaur, to examine the group's different types of adaptation to defence. Some—the great carnivores of the Jurassic and Cretaceous—passed over to the attack so as not to have to defend themselves. Others, like the little carnivores, *Iguanodons* and the duck-billed dinosaurs, found safety in flight, taking refuge when necessary in the depths of the waters. Others, again, found protection in their back plates and the strength of their tails, whether spined or not; this was the case with the *Stegosaurus* and *Ankylosaurus* which seem—at least *Stegosaurus* does—to have been able to roll up into a ball or to flatten itself against the earth, offering the enemy only an unassailable rampart of bony or horned plates. Finally, the horned dinosaurs, like our rhinoceros, seem to have practised both attack and defence, aided in this by their strong horns and by the collar that truly formed a protective shield.

Thus, when the various orders of dinosaur reached the ultimate point of their evolution, carnivorous forms with large teeth and herbivorous forms protected by large horns were face to face: simplifying this a little, one can say that *Tyrannosaurus* and *Triceratops* were face to face. The parallel between reptiles and mammals revealed by this specialization must be stressed: in fact, no animal has both powerful teeth and horns at the same time, only one or the other. This is the moment to emphasize that the reptiles of the Secondary and the mammals of the Tertiary have evolved by following completely comparable lines. At a distance of 150 million years, both have effected the conquest of the earth by almost the same means, occupying equally well the dry land and the air and the waters. To this phenomenon the paleontologists have given the name of "convergence."

Another important problem raised by the dinosaurs is that of their gigantism. As a result of recent studies, in particular the close examination of the casts of their brains, it certainly seems that we may attribute the great size of the majority of these reptilian forms to the great development of the pituitary gland. This ductless gland, which has very many functions, controls amongst other things the growth of the organism; medical men are familiar with cases of gigantism and acromegaly (abnormal size of the extremities, head, hands and feet) which are associated with the exaggerated activity of an enlarged pituitary.

Finally, a few words must be said concerning the manifest disproportion between the size of these dinosaurs and the size of their nervous systems. A typical example is that of *Stegosaurus* already cited: an animal of 6 tons, as big as an elephant but with a brain no greater than that of a two-months kitten. This is certainly an extreme case, but all the other dinosaurs had nothing to begrudge him. It is beyond doubt that, like the reptiles of to-day, the reptiles of the Secondary were relatively slow in their movements and reactions: the most active and lively of them led a slow life. At the beginning of this chapter some scenes of the Secondary world were described, but it is very necessary to realize that these scenes unfolded without haste and that no carnivorous reptile ever had to hurl itself upon a herbivorous reptile with the speed of a lion or a tiger upon its prey. On this Secondary earth, where neither the plants nor the animals were on our scale, gigantism was accompanied by unquestionable slowness. And this is probably one of the reasons (but we shall discuss the problem later) why the reptiles were supplanted by the very much smaller but much more agile mammals.

*

Among the forms deriving from the biped thecodonts were the flying reptiles and birds. Their development was a very important event in the history of life: vertebrates for the first time freed themselves from the servitude of weight and acquired the power of manoeuvring in the air.

To understand the importance of this achievement, the three following characteristics essential to all vertebrates aspiring to fly must be emphasized:

the fore-limbs had first of all to change into wings;

while retaining a strong skeleton and powerful muscles necessary for beating the wings, the body had to be lightened to the maximum, which was generally effected by a partial hollowing out of the bones;

the animal had to possess a nervous system sufficiently developed to be sensitive to a certain number of external influences, thereby assuring the animal a particularly acute sense of balance.

The first of these three conditions is very interesting, for it makes useful comparisons possible between the various groups of vertebrates that acquired the ability to fly. Actually, the transformation of the fore-limbs into wings was effected in three different ways in the three groups of flying vertebrates. In one group, the

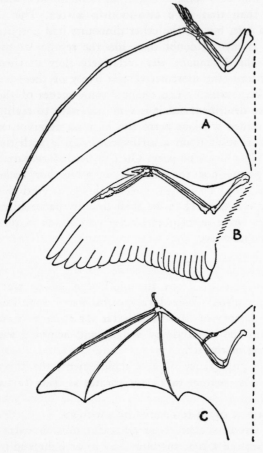

FIG. 78. Comparison of the wings of (*a*) flying reptiles, (*b*) birds, and (*c*) flying mammals.

reptiles, a membrane made its appearance between the very much lengthened last finger of the hand (our "little finger") and the body. Rather like a wing, this membrane permitted the animal to make gliding flights and the other fingers were transformed so as to end in hooked claws. With the birds, on the contrary, the whole arm was transformed, the fingers being united to form a single line of bone to support a membrane that was somewhat reduced in size. The long feathers fixed into this arm assured sustentation. Finally, the mammals effected their adaptation to flight by means of a membrane supported by four much lengthened fingers of the hand, the fifth finger—the thumb—being hooked and used by the animal to suspend itself upside down in the position characteristic of bats. It is in fact in this group of mammals that the transformation of the fore-limbs into wings was brought about.

The various types of mammals will be studied later and it will be sufficient here to examine rapidly the different forms of flying reptiles and the ancestors of the birds. All the flying reptiles belonged to the order Pterosauria, and lived in Europe, Africa, and North America. Most of their bones were hollow and the skull bones were welded into a solid mass in which it is difficult to recognize the separate bones. All this contributed to the lightening of the animal's body. The breast bone was very much enlarged and gave a very strong point of attachment to the pectoral muscles that moved the wings.

The majority of these reptiles must have been gliders, using the currents of warm air to sustain themselves, rather than real flying animals: in fact the wing, consisting only of a fairly fragile membrane stretched between the bones of the arm and the body, could not have had the same propulsive power as the wing of a bird or a bat. The pterosaurs of the Jurassic had many pointed teeth. Two main forms existed: *Rhamphorhynchus* with a long tail and the famous pterodactyl with a short tail. The flying reptiles of the Cretaceous were devoid of teeth and had short tails: the giant among them was *Pteranodon*, which had a wing-spread of about 25 feet.

Finally, we should note two special characteristics of these flying reptiles which make them like our modern birds. The brain was considerably developed as compared with the usual size of reptile brains; in fact flight requires a great development of the centres of vision, a development that is accompanied by a certain atrophy of the centres of smell. Further, it is not impossible that the Pterosauria were more or less "warm-blooded" animals (homeothermal); wing-movement requires a considerable expenditure of energy and it is among the birds that we find to-day the vertebrates with the highest internal temperature ($104°$ to $107.5°$ F.). It seems that on the tail of *Rhamphorhynchus* certain marks have been ob-

served that correspond to the sebaceous glands, which to-day are
always found at the roots of hairs, secreting a special fatty matter
that makes the hair more supple; therefore, if *Rhamphorhynchus*
had a hair system, at least on some part of its body, it was equipped
to counteract the loss of heat and therefore possessed a certain
power of thermal regulation. All the other reptiles—as has
been stated already—were, and still are, animals whose internal
temperature followed the variations of the external temperature (poecilothermal); moreover, their skin was bare, cov-

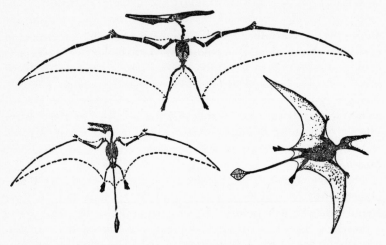

FIG. 79. *Above: Pteranodon:* with a wing-span of about 25 feet.
Below: left and right, *Rhamphorhynchus:* with a wing-span of
only 18 to 24 inches. (From *Discovery.*)

ered only with scales that could not protect them against loss of
heat.

The ancestors of the birds were curiously composite animals,
presenting simultaneously the features that ally them to the
reptiles (teeth and certain peculiarities of the skeleton) and others
that ally them to real birds (feathers, a skull formed of more or less
fused bones, and wings). Another feature of adaptation to flight
is very clear: the development in the brain of the visual areas at
the expense of the olfactory areas.

The first birds with teeth made their appearance in the Jurassic
in the form of *Archaeopteryx.* Von Mayer, a German naturalist,
discovered the outline of a feather near Solenhofen in Bavaria in

FIG. 80. The first of the birds with teeth: *Archaeopteryx*.

June 1861; it was imbedded in a bed of lithographic limestone, an extremely thin geological deposit formed at the bottom of lagoons, in which delicate structures like those of a feather are perfectly preserved. On August 15th of the same year the almost complete skeleton (only the head was missing) and several feathers of a bird were discovered; this remarkable skeleton is to-day at the Natural History Museum in London. In 1877 a second bird was discovered, this time with its head; it was purchased at once by the Berlin Museum.

These first ancestors of the birds would undoubtedly have been classed with the reptiles if the imprint of feathers had not been found beside their skeletons. *Archaeopteryx* was a bird the size of a pigeon. Oehmichen's studies of flight have shown that *Archae-opteryx* moved in the following way: it had to cling by its claws to a support, head down, exactly like our modern bats; then it let

FIG. 81. *Diatryma*: a giant bird of the Tertiary.

itself fall freely, which gave it the necessary impetus for flight. On the other hand, it was assisted by its long tail in clinging to trees or rocks like a wood-pecker and was thus able to perch upon a suitable starting point.

In the Cretaceous there was another ancestor of the birds, much more developed in the sense that the majority of its anatomical characteristics made it a real bird, except that it still had teeth. However, *Hesperornis* was a very specialized bird; a skilful swimmer and diving virtuoso, it had lost its wings. It was about 3 feet tall and was in every way comparable with modern penguins.

Later, in the Tertiary, appeared birds that were already modern, together with several birds of great size but devoid of wings, very like our ostriches, especially the celebrated *Diatryma* of the United States, which was 6 feet tall.

*

The crocodiles constitute the last group of Secondary reptiles deriving from the biped thecodonts, although at first sight this relationship might not be evident. To-day the crocodiles still represent an interesting order of the reptile class in that they have maintained a Secondary mode of life in surroundings very like Secondary surroundings for 150 million years. The first crocodiles made their appearance in the Jurassic, seeming to descend from one ancestor, *Protosuchus*, discovered in Arizona, almost assuring the passage on the anatomical plane between the thecodonts and the true crocodiles. In the Jurassic certain of these crocodiles, with paddle-like feet and flat rudder-like tails, led a marine life. Finally, in the Cretaceous there appeared small forms very like our modern crocodiles; but it was only at the beginning of the Tertiary that the existing forms appeared, alligators, caimans, gavials and crocodiles properly so-called, preceded meanwhile by a giant Cretaceous form, *Phobosuchus*, 50 feet long, with jaws about 6 feet long.

We have now passed in review the different evolutionary lines of the reptiles deriving from the small group of biped thecodonts. It remains to examine rapidly the other reptilian lines which derived, independently of each other, directly from Cotylosauria.

There is little to say of the turtles, which to-day represent a very specialized order of the reptile class. They are distinguished especially by their jaws, devoid of teeth and transformed into a horny beak, and by a carapace formed from the modified ribs: when the embryology of turtles is studied, it is observed that at a certain moment the increase in growth is very rapid and that the ribs, extending laterally, soon encircle the whole of the rest of the skeleton, as if inside a cage. One of the ancestors of our turtles, *Eunotosaurus*, has been found in South Africa and it dates from the end of the Triassic; its enlarged ribs stretched one behind the other and in contact, thus creating the beginning of the dorsal

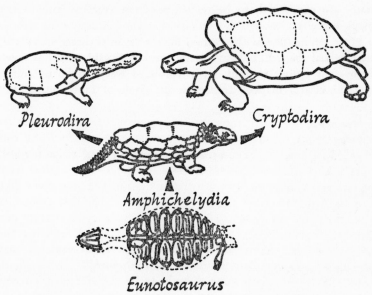

FIG. 82. The genealogical tree of the turtle: 150 million years ago *Eunotosaurus* already showed enlarged ribs which foreshadowed the joined plates of the future carapace.

plates of the carapace. A little later, in Europe, there lived another reptile, *Triassochelys*, which was already a normally formed turtle.

More interesting are the marine reptiles, but there is no point in spending much time on them, since their essential features have already been described at the beginning of this chapter. Some, by a typical phenomenon of convergence, had externally a very fish-like appearance: the Ichthyosaurs, of which it has been said that if they were seen alive to-day it would be difficult to distinguish them from sharks. The others, the Plesiosaurs, were like casks furnished with paddle-like limbs, a long tail and a long neck. Finally, *Mososaurus* and *Tylosaurus;* they looked like very long lizards, moving in the water by means of their flat paddle-like limbs; they were veritable sea-serpents.

In the seas of the Jurassic they were the neighbours of the marine crocodile known as *Geosaurus.* They were to be found especially in the Secondary seas together with those strange molluscs, the ammonites. For although in the vertebrate domain the Secondary era could be called the Age of Reptiles, it ought, so far as inverte- brates are concerned, to be regarded as the Age of Ammonites, which literally swarmed in every ocean. The ammonites are found in great abundance in the terrain dating from the Secondary era; their helical shape has always made them noticeable and has given them their name. In fact, their fossilized shells make us think, by their clearly marked transverse divisions, of rams' horns, and

FIG. 83. An ammonite, a typical mollusc of the Secondary seas.

the early naturalists so named them in memory of the ram that accompanied Jupiter Ammon in Greek mythology.

They were for a long time thought to be petrified serpents and were regarded as of great value either as medicine or charms. Ammonites were very often used in decorating monuments and in the sixteenth century Canon Bartole d'Anjou had one embedded in the lintel of a small door leading to the towers of Bayeux Cathedral.

Zoologically, the ammonites were molluscs belonging to the cephalopod class, which also includes octopuses, cuttle-fish and squids. They therefore ranked with the most highly developed invertebrates, especially so far as their nervous system was con- cerned. They lived inside a shell, just like the modern nautilus, which is, moreover, a survivor from the Tertiary. To understand how the shell grew, one must imagine that the ammonite lived inside a shell chamber a little after the fashion of our snails, except

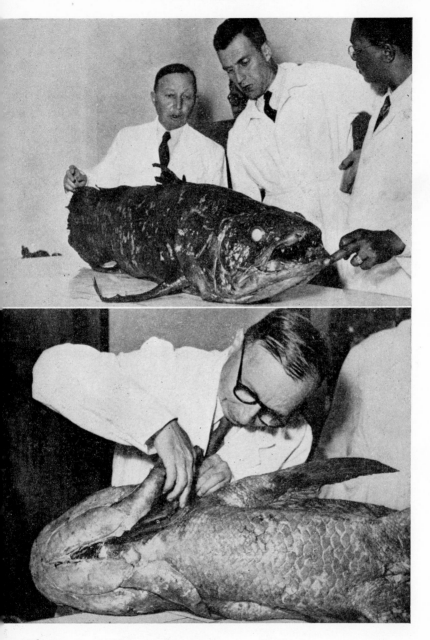

(*above*):
Professor Millot (*left*) and his assistants with the first Coelacanth to be
examined in a good state of preservation.
(*below*):
The Coelacanth here reveals one of its main anatomical peculiarities:
its pectoral fin, the rays being supported by what is really a small limb.
(Service Général de l'Information, Madagascar.)

The most terrible of the carnivorous reptiles of the Cretaceous period:
Tyrannosaurus, reaching a height of 50 feet.

Three enormous "boars" (*Diniohyrus*) of the Miocene period.
(Paintings by C. R. Knight, Chicago Natural History Museum.)

that during its life the ammonite secreted a partition that separated an empty compartment at the end of the shell from an inhabited compartment opening to the outside. The secretion of successive partitions thus led the shell to be divided into many compartments of which the animal occupied the last. The outlines of these partitions are always very visible on the fossil shell.

During the 150 million years of the Secondary era the ammonites, like reptiles, evolved in different directions. This is no place to examine even rapidly the different orders and different families in the midst of which these cephalopods divided. It will suffice simply to indicate their two main evolutionary tendencies. On the one hand, while at the beginning of the Secondary they showed simple partitions, these gradually became more complicated, with hollows and swellings that were ornamented with scallops; these various patterns on the partitions, known to paleontologists as sutures, permit us to identify the different families and genera.

On the other hand, with the passing of the Secondary era, we find the ammonites uncurling, and at the end of the Cretaceous we find that the majority of them are no longer formed like small coils but as crooks, of which the uncoiled end is slightly curved.

*

Finally, from Cotylosauria arose a last line of reptiles, that which led to the mammals. It will not be studied in this chapter but will form the introduction to the next. It is sufficient for the moment to remember that from the reptiles of the Secondary era came the birds and the mammals. It is in this sense that one can say that these two groups of vertebrates both passed through the reptile stage, regarding the reptiles not as a properly individualized class but as an evolutionary stage.

*

But this very diversified world of the Secondary reptiles had its term. After having reigned over the planet for 150 million years the reptiles were abruptly extinguished, leaving as evidence of their splendid past only a number of relatively small species, crocodiles, serpents, lizards and turtles.

Though not exceptional in paleontology, this disappearance of a group so varied, the representatives of which were masters of all the habitable regions, is nevertheless surprising, especially as it was effected with great rapidity. It all took place like the scene-changing in certain theatres: in a few million years (a very short time, geologically speaking) the stage revolved, the decor of the Tertiary occupied the scene, the reptiles were finally whisked away into the wings and the mammals took the lead, replacing the failing reptiles with much more success.

To explain this extinction we must discuss a number of arguments that come under four main headings. Some people have suggested that a particularly deadly epidemic attacked the dinosaurs at the end of the Secondary (one can reflect on the present epidemic of myxomatosis which decimated the rabbits in 1954); but this is pure hypothesis, unsupported by any scientific verification. Others have sought to connect the disappearance of the dinosaurs with their gigantism, that is to say, with a hypersecretion of the pituitary hormones; actually, it is a fact that in paleontology gigantism seems to toll the bell for the orders or families that are overtaken by it. A sickness of the ductless glands has also been suggested, but there, too, no indisputable proof can be provided.

Still others stress the disproportion between the small and rudimentary brain of the dinosaurs and the enormous size of their bodies. In this respect a comparison between the reptiles and the mammals is justified, one of the main characteristics of the latter being the relatively great size of the highly differentiated nervous system as compared with the other organs. Furthermore, the reptiles were animals with a variable internal temperature and the mammals were animals with a constant internal temperature. With "cold blood" is associated the relative immobility of the reptiles and their great liability to fatigue, while the "warm-blooded" animals can move very quickly and find, in the cellular combustion which takes place at a rapid pace, the energy necessary to recuperate very easily.

For it must not be forgotten that at the end of the Cretaceous and the beginning of the Tertiary, great geological changes were taking place: the surface of the earth had been disrupted by the upthrust of the alpine chains, the Himalayas, the Rocky Mountains, and so on; the climates changed quite violently, too, and the average temperature fell, resulting in a profound transformation of the flora. All the reptiles were affected by these changes; the herbivores found their favourite plants more difficult to get than before, and less directly, the carnivores suffered too. Having great powers of adaptation, thanks among other things to their thermal regulation and their more responsive nervous system, the mammals were better equipped than the reptiles to face up to these new conditions. It is justifiable to explain—in part, at least—the extinction of the reptiles by the competition of the mammals. It was the triumph of mind over matter, so to speak.

In conclusion, when attempting to explain the abrupt disappearance of the reptiles at the end of the Secondary, the fact must not be forgotten that zoological groups, just like individuals, seem to experience a period of youth, followed by an adult period, then a period of old age, a phenomenon known by the more or less suitable name of racial senescence. This racial senescence reveals itself at the moment when the groups begin to specialize very strictly. This should always be remembered when trying to account for the extinction of the dinosaurs at the end of the Secondary; two other factors to be taken into consideration are the reptiles' small capacity for adaptation when faced with new climatic and ecological conditions created by the geological changes that marked the beginning of the Tertiary, and the competition of the mammals.

CHAPTER VII

The Penultimate Conquest of the World

WHILE the throne of France was tottering to its fall, and while
the Terror was at its height, on the Normandy coast a young man
of about 20 was quietly fishing for crabs, sea-urchins and other
strange creatures and studying them in peace. About 15 years
later this young man had become Baron Georges Cuvier, and as
Professor at the Imperial Museum of Natural History he had in-
vited a few particularly competent naturalists to his office. He
showed them a small slab of stone, a little longer than it was wide,
on the surface of which a small skeleton was outlined: a long and
delicate head could clearly be distinguished and jaws with short
pointed teeth, also the vertebral column and the four limbs. This
was unquestionably the skeleton of a small opossum embedded in

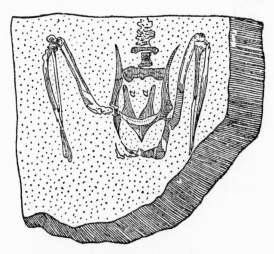

FIG. 84. Cuvier's opossum (*a*, the marsupial bones).

gypsum, that had lived about 50 million years ago at the spot
where the hill of Montmartre now stands. Cuvier then began his
demonstration: since this was an opossum and therefore a marsupial, it should be possible to find at the level of the pelvis the
two small bones which in all marsupials support the familiar
pouch where the young live after they are born. Now these bones
were not visible on the slab that Cuvier held in his hand. According to the general appearance of the skeleton they should be found
a few millimetres below the surface and at a spot which Cuvier
pointed out to his audience. Then, taking up a slender steel blade,
he gently scraped the stone and in a few moments revealed the
two small flat branches of the marsupial bones.

Founded by Georges Cuvier, paleontology and comparative
anatomy had just come into being.

*

Georges Léopold Chrétien Frédéric Dagobert Cuvier, who passed
into posterity under the name of Georges Cuvier, was born at Montbéliard in 1769, the second son of a retired non-commissioned
officer of Louis XV's armies. In 1769 Montbéliard was already a
small administrative capital of some importance, since it had been
for a long time the seat of the small Duchy of Montbéliard which,
after having been attached to France for a century, was at this time
a dependency of the German prince who ruled over the Duchy of
Württemberg. So it was not surprising that the young Cuvier,
after very creditable studies in his native town, should go to
continue them as an exhibitioner at Stuttgart. Georges had already
shown a lively taste for the natural sciences and it is said that at a
very early age, very much interested by Buffon's *Histoire générale
des animaux* which he had found among his mother's books, he
had coloured them all with crayon. At Stuttgart, he was a very
brilliant student and continued to interest himself especially in
zoology. But he soon had to abandon the Academy and in 1788,
when he was 19, he took a post as tutor at the home of the Comte
d'Héricy, whose property was in Normandy, near Valmont. This
stay in Normandy was very important for Cuvier from several
points of view. First of all, because he was able to collect very
many marine animals on this coast where the fauna is particularly
rich and abundant; it was there that he acquired his zoological
training in the very many dissections, descriptions and sketches

he was able to carry through with tireless patience and a great
capacity for work. It was in Normandy, too, that, with the help
of the only book on zoology in the Count's library, Linnaeus'
Systema Naturae of 1735, he learned or revised all the zoological
knowledge of his day, and often, without fully realizing it, clarified very many points concerning the zoology of marine animals
and so made some important discoveries.

In Normandy, moreover, he made the acquaintance of the Abbé
Tessier, an expert in agronomy and former encyclopedist, who
lived there more or less secretly in order to escape the persecutions
of the Terror. He was very interested by Cuvier's work, encour-
aged him in his researches and occasionally gave him advice; then,
as soon as he could, the Abbé Tessier put Cuvier in touch by
letter with the most eminent zoologists of the time. Astonished
by this young man's zoological knowledge, Saint-Hilaire made
him come to Paris and in 1795, at the age of 26, obtained for him
the post of Professor of Zoology at the Ecole Centrale du Panthéon in Paris. He continued his researches while he conducted
his courses, the documentation, clarity and novelty of which soon
made him famous. The result was that in the following year, when
only 27 years old, he was appointed deputy to the Professor of
Anatomy at the Museum, a function which he soon combined
with that of Professor at the Collège de France. Moreover, he was
elected a member of the Institut de France. On January 21st, 1796,
he presented to the Academy of Science the famous paper in
which he compared the species now living with the "extinct or
lost" species. This was the first time, except perhaps in some of
Buffon's chapters, that anyone had dared publicly to proclaim,
without being regarded as a visionary or insane, that the world
had not always looked the same, that there had once been species,
now known only by their fossil remains, very different from
existing species both in their anatomical structure and in the way
they lived.

In 1798, from the lessons in zoology that he had been giving
for three years, he produced his *Tableaux élémentaires de l'histoire
naturelle des animaux*, a basic work in which classification of the
animal kingdom and the diagnostic characters of various groups
were set forth. Finally, in 1802, when he was 33, Georges Cuvier
became Professor of Anatomy at the Natural History Museum.
Then it was that he was able to give his best: he undertook noth-

ing more nor less than the systematic study of the anatomy of all the vertebrates.

Shortly afterwards there came into his hands by chance some small fossil bones of which, he was told, a considerable number were to be found in the gypsum quarries of the Paris region, especially at Montmartre. Then Cuvier, helped by his friend Alexandre Brongniart, carried out a systematic exploration of all the places where gypsum was extracted. He was soon in possession of a hundred bones and teeth, but very often fragmentary. He had a real puzzle to solve: if he wanted to reconstitute the fauna of this vanished age, he had to discover which bones went together, which teeth went with which bones, which heads went with which limbs, and so on. Here, therefore, is the jig-saw puzzle to which he devoted himself in order to resuscitate two of the principal species whose skeletons were found in the Montmartre gypsum.

He was faced with a certain number of anatomical fragments which he had to assemble in order to reconstitute a complete animal. First of all there were the teeth: some molars, all more or less alike, thick-set, massive, and bearing two or three crescent-shaped crests forming the concentric arcs of a circle, but so worn that the tops had given place to two lines of enamel marking the boundaries of a ridge of ivory, pointed at each end; then some canines, some of which were very long and certainly projected above the level of the molars, while others were of more modest size and did not project. Besides this collection of teeth were some flat bones which, patiently assembled, made possible the reconstruction of the essential parts of two heads (the bones of the face and cranium); one of these heads bore a close resemblance to that of a modern camel, while the other, with nasal bones developed in such a way that one could not but suspect the existence of a short trunk, was like the head of a tapir. The final pieces of the puzzle were the more or less complete limbs, on which there were sometimes two and sometimes three toes.

Cuvier's first conclusion was that all the molars were alike and completely comparable with those of a modern rhinoceros, so that these animals from the Montmartre gypsum must first of all be regarded as herbivorous, and next as pachyderms. But since there were two kinds of canines it had to be admitted that two species of herbivorous pachyderms existed side by side. To that which

combined the molars of a rhinoceros and the low canines he gave
the name *Anoplotherium* which means "wild beast without
weapons" and to the other, which was provided with projecting
canines, he gave the name *Palaeotherium,* which means "old wild
beast." But the next stage in this game was to assign the teeth to
the skulls. It was to *Palaeotherium* that Cuvier assigned the canines
that rose above the dental surface because in modern tapirs the
canines always projected in some degree. By the process of elimina-
tion, it was to the camel-headed *Anoplotherium* that he assigned
the jaws with the smaller canines; furthermore, this hypothesis agreed very well with zoological information, since camels
do not have canines rising very far above the dental surface.

It was finally necessary to assign the two groups of recon-
structed feet to the two heads which have just been described.
Cuvier had already established that some of these feet had two
toes and others had three. Now the herbivores mostly have the
same number of toes on both fore- and hind-feet (for example, in
the horse one toe in front and one toe behind; in the camel two
toes in front and two toes behind; in the elephant five toes in front
and five behind). Cuvier therefore decided that the herbivorous
pachyderm he had undertaken to study had the same number of
toes on both the fore and hind limbs. Consequently, he decided to
assign all the limbs with three toes to the head with the small trunk
and to assign to the same head the projecting canines, such as exist
in the modern tapir. This ancestor of the tapir was therefore
Palaeotherium. To the camel skull he assigned the short canines
and the limbs with two toes: this was *Anoplotherium.* Thus, skilfully sorting out the collection of a hundred bones and teeth, often
incomplete, Cuvier was able to reconstruct in their general lines
the skeletons of two herbivores that disappeared 50 million years
ago.

He had scarcely revealed the identity of these two reconstructions than a complete skeleton was discovered in the Montmartre
gypsum. This skeleton was that of *Palaeotherium* and, apart from
some minute details, it was entirely similar to the one which
Cuvier had reconstituted. The skeleton is exhibited to-day in the
paleontological gallery of the Natural History Museum in Paris
and it is very striking to see beside it the two sketches made by
Cuvier before it was discovered. Equally striking is the attitude

of this *Palaeotherium* with its twisted feet and outstretched neck, and its head thrown back, an attitude which has led certain experts to agree that the animal had died by sinking slowly into the mud, desperately thrusting its nostrils upwards to breathe its last gasps of air.

This example is typical of the method perfected by Cuvier in the study and reconstruction of fossilized vertebrates. Probably only his impressive knowledge of anatomy and zoology had made it possible for him to carry out such a task. But by doing so Cuvier

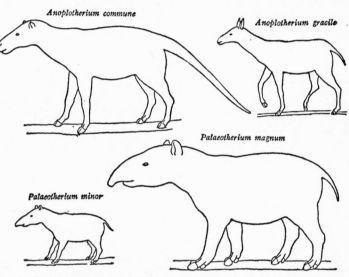

FIG. 85. Cuvier's reconstructions of the mammals in the Montmartre gypsum.

really established two new sciences: paleontology and comparative anatomy. In comparative anatomy Cuvier had quite simply discovered the principle of the correlation according to which, concerning any animal, *"chaque partie peut être donnée par chaque autre et toutes par une,"* as he himself said. Thus, if for example one considers a cat, or in a more general way the carnivores (lion, tiger, panther, bear, dog, wolf, fox, etc.) one always associates them with long and pointed canines, flat molars, high and sharp, toes that end in claws, and many other anatomical characteristics; one cannot conceive of a carnivore with feet ending in little hoofs, or with sharp canines as well as molars made for grinding. On the other hand, if one considers a herbivore like a horse or a cow, one immediately associates it with sharp incisors, small canines or even none at all, and strong, flat, rough molars, while the feet, which are no longer instruments for attack but organs of defence in the sense that they make it possible for the animal to flee, are long and slender and end in hoofs. These are two typical examples, a little simplified, of course, of what can be drawn from this law of correlations which forms the basis of comparative anatomy.

It was by listening to "the voice of comparative anatomy," to use his own words, that Cuvier founded paleontology, and in so doing directed it into extremely original channels which clearly marked the work of the very important French school throughout the nineteenth century. In studying the fauna of the Montmartre gypsum, Cuvier was not content to sort out a few fragments of bone and tie them together with iron wires in order subsequently to write a dry description that would be discouraging to a layman and even an expert would have to read carefully; he wanted to devote himself to a real resurrection of the past, and on one occasion regretted that he had not the "omnipotent trumpet" at his disposal.

Anoplotherium, a creature with the teeth of a rhinoceros, the head of a camel, and feet with two hoofed toes, shows clearly the spirit in which Cuvier worked. The geologists have established that gypsum is a sediment deposited at Montmartre, and elsewhere in the Paris region, by invasions of the sea. *Anoplotherium* therefore lived by the edge of the water in the briny lagoons or marshes. Furthermore, he had a long tail. Cuvier found these two facts enough to establish that *Anoplotherium*, like the otters, must very often have lived in the water, where it found its essential food in the form of aquatic plants, since it was a herbivorous mammal. Further, pursuing the analogy, he gave *Anoplotherium* smooth hair like the otter, even a naked or partly naked skin like the hippopotamus. Finally, he gave *Anoplotherium* the very much reduced ears which are the attribute of all aquatic animals (otherwise it would have been hindered in diving and swimming). Without doubt Cuvier exaggerated a little, for nothing proves that the anatomy of *Anoplotherium* answered to the details of this description, although one must agree that it had semi-aquatic habits. But this description admirably illustrates the way Cuvier's mind worked; in a few years he really brought to life before the eyes of his contemporaries the 50-million-year-old fauna that haunted the marshes at the spot where the hill of Montmartre now rises to-day.

*

The essential works of Cuvier were published in five volumes in 1812 and 1813; four of them dealt with mammals. In 1828 he published his *Natural History of Fishes,* and in 1830 his *History of Natural Science.* He died of cholera on May 13th, 1832, during an epidemic that had spread from Poland and Russia. But before he died, Cuvier had known during 30 years all the honours to which a man might aspire. Little interested in politics, he showed great flexibility towards the different regimes, a flexibility which contrasted sharply with the obstinacy he showed towards his scientific opponents, even when it was a matter of detail. Thus, undaunted and triumphant, he pursued his career under three different regimes: the Revolution, the Napoleonic Empire and the Restoration.

One is often very vexed with Cuvier, not for his attitude towards the political powers, but for his scientific attitude when faced with certain problems, of which the principal was transformism. It is in this respect that Cuvier's career is often contrasted with that of one of his colleagues at the Museum, the Professor of Zoology, Jean Baptiste de Lamarck, who in 1809 had expounded his theories in *Philosophie zoologique.* The career of this enthusiastic military man, who became a botanist by accident and a professor of zoology by chance, will be described in due course, but it is sufficient to say here that in his views of life on the earth Lamarck was fundamentally opposed to Cuvier. It was Cuvier's view that the vanished species he had resuscitated had been wiped off the surface of the globe following a gigantic cataclysm, after which new animal and vegetable species had peopled the earth. But for Lamarck, doubtless due in part to the fact that he knew plants and invertebrates better than the vertebrates (it was exactly the converse with Cuvier), there had been no successive revolutions; living things slowly and progressively changed from one to another, the more simple forms preceding the more complex. Cuvier was the champion of discontinuity and he succeeded in getting his ideas accepted thanks to the fame he had acquired by his brilliant researches. Lamarck was the champion of continuity but, more modest and less brilliant, and working less in the public eye, he was totally ignored by his contemporaries, was even ridiculed, and acquired prestige only with the English geologists, especially Charles Lyell. Moreover, it was through Lyell that Darwin absorbed Lamarck's ideas and thereby brought transformism to success in scientific circles throughout the world. By his violently anti-transformist attitude Cuvier doubtless hindered to some extent the development of certain branches of biology in France. But the credit of having laid the essential foundations of paleontology and comparative anatomy can never be taken from him. In fact, following Cuvier's discoveries, and using the research methods he had brought to perfection, the world's paleontologists set out in pursuit of the fossil vertebrates.

In France the paleontological school was very brilliant and, not having space here to name all the experts, we will mention only one, Albert Gaudry, who first of all studied the fossil mammals of Greece, and afterwards those present in many beds in France, especially the curious fauna in the phosphorite pockets in the Quercy chalk and the mammals in the terraces of the Somme near Amiens and Abbeville. In America, besides Cope, who became famous especially for his study of fossil reptiles, we must mention Osborn for his remarkable work on vanished pachyderms. Moreover, all these authors and their pupils were quickly won over to transformism and did much for the propagation of these ideas.

Thus the grouping of fossil faunas gradually took shape. As they came back to life they could be seen to take their places in the landscapes which geology and paleobotany have enabled us to imagine with very great accuracy, so that to-day two main tendencies are developing in the 150-year-old science of paleontology. On the one hand, as all the fossils of the principal countries have been to all intents and purposes studied in their smallest details and the beds that held them are also well known to the geologists, attention is being given to the reconstruction of the environments in which these fossil animals evolved, and to finding out how these animals that vanished millions of years ago lived, were born and died, what they ate, how they reproduced themselves, and so on. In this way the paleontologist now seeks to pursue the science of ecology (the study of living things in relation to their environment) and ethnology (the study of habits).

On the other hand, new fossils are being sought in regions where scientific expeditions are very difficult to organize; in other words, to extend the field of paleontological research and to cover the whole world. Thus in 1948, for example, at the cost of a very difficult exploration, the Russians found in Siberia a splendid series of reptiles in process of transition between reptiles properly so-called and mammals; this series has helped to fill the gaps in two related series discovered not many years ago, partly in the Rocky Mountains and partly in South Africa, the excavations in South Africa having been done around 1930 by Broom, who is better known for his discoveries of a great number of members of the *Australopithecus* family, the ape-men of the Kalahari desert.

*

It was precisely these new techniques of comparative anatomy, perfected by Cuvier, that in the long run made the triumph of transformism possible. They have revealed the conditions of the transition from the fish to the amphibians, then from the amphibians to the reptiles, thereby describing the means by which the continents were conquered. It is with the aid of comparative anatomy that, pausing to study the fossil reptiles of Siberia, South Africa and North America, we can now describe how the penultimate conquest of the world by the mammals was prepared.

Richard Owen, the most famous of Cuvier's successors, was the first to have insisted on the strange relationship between the reptiles and the mammals when, about 1850, he heard from South Africa about the remains of a reptile 200 million years old, consisting mainly of the bones of the skull. Born in 1804, Richard Owen pursued an eventless career, very comparable to that of his master Cuvier in that he quickly climbed all the stages of university life smoothly and without a struggle, teaching and doing research work simultaneously. He later turned to medicine and, having obtained his diploma, entered the Royal College of Surgeons in London as a professor. But, devoting himself to the study of anatomy, Owen was very soon attracted to paleontology after becoming acquainted with the work of the French experts, and it was in this field eventually that he especially shone. Very soon he was specializing in the study of fossil vertebrates and soon after that he brought his attention to bear upon reptiles. It was he who in 1842 invented the name "dinosaur" for the giant reptiles that were becoming well known by the middle of the nineteenth century. Soon he was appointed Director of the Natural History Department of the British Museum in London, which had just been created; in this capacity he excelled and was able to arrange for the transfer of his work to the large building at South Kensington where the collections could be shown to the public in their entirety and with proper artistic care. Under the stimulus of its first director the Museum enriched itself with large collections of stuffed animals, skeletons and fossil casts.

About 1850, as an expert on fossil reptiles, Owen received the most important parts of a skeleton from South Africa. He had scarcely begun to examine them when he was struck by the fact that this creature showed a curious mixture of reptilian features and those which until then had been regarded as peculiar to the mammals. It was a reptile in its general appearance, but when certain details of its skeleton were considered, especially the bones

FIG. 86. *Dicynodon:* half reptile, half mammal.

of the head, Owen could not fail to be struck by the clearly mammalian characteristics. The first thing to be observed was that the teeth were slightly differentiated, in the sense that there was a typical canine, a real fang, contrasting with teeth constructed for grinding that could already qualify as molars; there were no teeth to qualify as incisors, but there was a horned beak like that to be found in some of the fossil herbivorous reptiles. Now this differentiation of the teeth into several distinct types is characteristic of the mammals, whereas in reptiles all the teeth are always alike. Further, still considering the head of this South African mammal, Owen observed the existence of a zygomatic arch, that is to say that sort of bony bridge that starts from the temporal bone, in front of the inner auricular duct, and ends at the level of the cheek: this, too, is a typical feature of mammals. He noted also the anatomical configuration of the bones of the nasal region, which was exactly like that of that strange Australian beaked mammal *Ornithorhynchus* (the duck-billed platypus). Finally, he stressed the existence of a thin bony plate which formed a sort of second palate partially lining the floor of the nasal cavities: it was a rudimentary secondary palate which one finds complete in mammals. The general appearance of the head led Owen to call this strange composite fossil *Dicynodon*, because of its fairly considerable resemblance to the skull of a dog.

The other parts of the skeleton in Owen's possession made it possible for him to describe *Dicynodon* as a carnivorous quadruped the size of a small bear and to emphasize the very definite kinship between the pelvis of this reptile and that of certain modern mammals. With an audacity that was admirable considering this was 100 years ago, Owen declared that it was necessary to seek the origins of modern and fossil mammals in the heart of certain reptile groups. And now, during the last 20 years, important

Fig. 87. *Dimetrodon:* a carnivorous reptile with some mammalian features.

excavations carried out in North America, Siberia and South Africa have fully confirmed this hypothesis by revealing a whole series of fossil reptile forms which have established an almost continuous link between reptiles and mammals, to the extent that of some of these species one can justifiably ask whether they are still reptiles or already mammals.

It was something like 200 million years ago, in the Permian, that appeared the first animals to evolve in this direction, the principal types being fairly abundant both in North America (Texas) and in France (the Autun region), as well as in various parts of the North Atlantic continent. The most curious of these Pelycosaurs was the carnivorous *Dimetrodon*, which had long spines on its back that were none other than the abnormally elongated projections of certain dorsal vertebrae, serving as a framework for a sort of membranous sail which could fold down on the back or to stand up vertically at will. Some have tried to assign a protective role to this great sail, which could reach to a yard high on an animal which was only 2 yards long: carnivorous animals could not have attacked it without getting these long spines in their mouths. Actually this hypothesis is very thin, for it seems that the *Dimetrodon* was just about the most carnivorous of all the carnivores of the Permian fauna of Texas. Others have put forward a more fanciful explanation: they have imagined the *Dimetrodon* navigating the lakes with the help of this sail which it was able to trim at will according to the direction of the winds. Actually it is probably unnecessary to seek any functional explana-

FIG. 88. *Moschops:* a curious reptile with clearly differentiated teeth.

tion whatever and one has only to admit quite simply the existence of the organ and no more. Similar membranous sails, supported by spiny apophyses of the dorsal vertebrae, are also found in other Pelycosauria, like the herbivorous *Edaphosaurus,* as well as in the modern chameleon. Although these Pelycosauria are still definitely reptilian in the aggregate of their characteristics, they took a step in the direction of the mammals in the structure and reciprocal disposition of certain bones of the skull. In the fine Russian *Dinocephalus* series two characteristics appeared that were new in reptiles: instead of the legs growing at right angles from the body, the humerus and the femur being parallel to the earth in such a way that the elbow and knee were very far from the body, the limbs became parallel to the body, all their bones being aligned one after the other in a perpendicular line to the earth.

Amphibians, the "classic" reptiles and the Pelycosauria moved with limbs apart, while the reptiles of mammalian appearance and the mammals themselves moved "elbows to side," just like we do.

Dinocephalus also showed three clearly differentiated kinds of teeth: incisors, canines and molars, which is definitely a mammalian characteristic. So we find, 175 to 200 million years ago, carnivorous forms like the Siberian *Inostranzevia*, a kind of serpent 10 feet long, with stumpy limbs and a tiger's head, and herbivorous forms like the South African *Moschops*, a rhinoceros-like creature with a giraffe's neck and thick, short limbs.

Finally we come to the Theriodontia of the Triassic, 175 million years old, with clearly differentiated teeth, with two successive dentitions (the milk teeth and the adult teeth), and a secondary palate more clearly formed in the later specimens. It is in a deposit in the Karroo, in the northern regions of South Africa, that we can best follow the stages of this progressive transformation. First of all we find *Ericiolacerta,* a large and heavy quadruped, prototype of the group sometimes called the "reptiles with cats' whiskers" because some have thought that in the holes in the cheek-bones were the channels for the nerves which, in cats and other Felidae, coupled with the long stiff hairs of the moustache, give these animals an additional sense of touch. Actually it seems wiser to regard these as orifices through which the blood vessels and nerves supplying the facial muscles passed. These facial muscles are another mammalian feature, being almost totally missing from either fossil or modern reptiles.

Almost contemporaneous with *Ericiolacerta* was *Cynognathus,* a sort of large bear with a skull anatomically exactly like that of a mammal; it also had three different sorts of teeth and, since its vertebral column was divided into three distinct regions, one must attribute to it the possession of a diaphragm. Finally, still in South Africa, in the very old Jurassic terrains dating from 150 million years ago, a quite small reptile the size of a rat has been discovered: *Karoomys,* all the characteristics of which are those of a mammal, excepting the articulation of the mandible to the base of the skull and the articulation of the skull to the vertebral column.

It is necessary to emphasize this last point, for it concerns a vital factor. In fact, the paleontologists have often to establish their criteria of identification on complex anatomical structures,

and since the appearance of the mammals is an important event in
the history of life, we shall have to stress the differences between
mammals and reptiles.

The most obvious diagnostic difference is in the covering of the
skin and no great effort is needed to contrast the reptiles, which
are covered with scales, with the mammals, which are covered
with hair. Another characteristic is also well known, since our
revulsion from reptiles is often due to the fact that they feel cold:
reptiles are animals of variable temperature, whereas mammals are
animals with a temperature that remains constant. If we now take
our attention to the teeth, we note that those of mammals are
divided into three categories. There are the incisors for cutting,
the canines for biting and the molars for grinding; further, in
mammals there are two successive dentitions, first the milk teeth
and then the adult teeth. But in reptiles the teeth, which are often
very numerous, are all of the same type and when a tooth is worn
out it is discarded and another grows in its place.

Other differences between reptiles and mammals are more sub-
tle, because they arise from anatomical characteristics that are
not assimilable at first glance. One of these essential characteristics
concerns the formation of the lower jaw, the mandible as it is
known to the experts, and the way it is articulated with the rest of
the head. In reptiles the mandible is actually made up of three
different bones, which are arranged in line and fused together: the
first of these bones carries the teeth and is therefore known as the
dentary, the second is the angular and is so named because of the
shape it takes in some inferior vertebrates, and the third is the
articular, the bone which serves to articulate the jaw with the skull
by means of a fourth small bone called the quadrate. In mammals
this anatomical structure is extremely simplified in that the
dentary alone forms the whole mandible and articulates directly
with the base of the skull. Of the three other bones present in
reptiles, the angular simply disappears, while the articular and
quadrate form part of the chain of ossicles of the middle ear; in
fact, the vibrations of the tympanum produced by sounds are
transmitted to the inner ear (which is accommodated inside the
temporal bone and is the organ of hearing properly speaking)
through a set of small ossicles aligned one behind the other and
called respectively malleus (or hammer, which corresponds to the
articular), incus (or anvil, which corresponds to the quadrate),

stapes (or stirrup, which corresponds to the columella auris or hyomandibula).

Still in the field of cranial anatomy, the skull of a mammal moves on the vertebral column through the medium of two bony bosses known as the occipital condyles, the presence of which permits the head to move in almost all directions and especially from right to left, and up and down. On the contrary, in reptiles the skull moves on the vertebral column by one condyle only, singularly limiting the movements of the head, which is practically in one piece with the vertebral column. Two other differences should be noted. One is the appearance in mammals of a bony partition lining the floor of the nasal cavities to form what is called the palate, which is actually a secondary palate. The other is the differentiation of the vertebral column into quite distinct

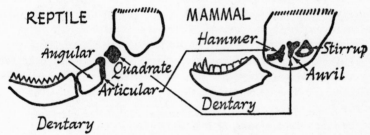

FIG. 89. The articulation of the jaw in reptiles and mammals.

regions, known as cervical, dorsal, lumbar, sacral and coccygeal. To this differentiation is connected the existence of a muscular partition, known as the diaphragm, separating the thoracic cage from the abdominal cavity.

Paleontology and comparative anatomy thus reveal the existence 200 million years ago of creatures intermediate between reptiles and mammals. But some of these creatures still exist to-day to bear witness through some of their characteristics to the reptilian origin of mammals. This curious composite creature, *Ornithorhynchus* (duck-billed platypus), with the flat beak and webbed feet of a duck, the body of an otter, the tail of a beaver and the claws of a dog, is to be found in Australia. It lays eggs and some regard this as sufficient reason not to allow it the name of mammal. However, although the females have no udders properly speaking, they nevertheless secrete milk; all the small lacteal ducts open

by a simple orifice at the ventral skin level and it is by sucking
the hairs, which become bunched together like the hairs of a paint-
brush dipped in liquid fat, that the young feed. In Tasmania,
and therefore not far away from *Ornithorhynchus*, lives *Echidna*
(spiny ant-eater); this animal, which is curiously covered with
spines, like a hedgehog or porcupine, cannot be denied the name
of mammal, since it nurses its young; but it must be admitted
that it is an extremely primitive mammal, with some characteristics
that are very definitely reptilian. One of these characteristics is
well defined by the very name of the group to which these two
curious creatures belong, monotremes, that is to say, "animals
with only one orifice." In fact, as in reptiles and also in birds, the
intestine, the urinary passage and the genital passage all open

FIG. 90. (Left) *Ornithorhynchus*, or duck-billed platypus;
(right) *Tachyglossus*, or five-toed *Echidna*. Two egg-laying
mammals (monotremes) from Australia. (From Young's
Life of the Vertebrates.)

into a cloaca and communicate with the exterior through it; but
in the more developed mammals these three systems—digestive,
urinary and genital—open separately to the exterior, or at least
they do in the female. Another characteristic which clearly distinguishes monotremes is the laying of eggs. It was through the
shell egg that reptiles succeeded in escaping from servitude to
an equatic life that was obligatory to their ancestors the amphibians,
but in mammals reproduction achieves its perfect form in the
sense that the young are protected in the body of the mother,
sheltered from all external dangers, until they are able to face the
external world. Thus vertebrate reproduction reaches its final perfection in mammals and gives them a total liberty of movement
over the surface of the continents.

But it is in relation to reproduction that the difference between

reptiles and mammals is most clearly revealed; the matter turns on
the existence in mammals of a placenta that closely unites the
fetus to its mother. It is again from Australia that we obtain the
main information on this subject.

In fact, for 150 million years, throughout the Secondary, when
the gigantic herbivorous and carnivorous reptiles ruled the world,
there lived between their feet, so to speak, tiny mammals that
descended apparently from creatures very like the South African
Karoomys: the oldest known of these mammals—known moreover only by a single jaw—was *Tritylodon*, which had molars
covered with many small protuberances and was thus the prototype of the Multituberculata. These Multituberculata lived very
quietly until the beginning of the Tertiary. Very little is known
about them except that their minute size enabled them to escape
the teeth of the carnivorous reptiles and that, very little specialized,
they developed slowly while their reptile cousins dominated the

FIG. 91. The jaw, still little differentiated, of one of the first
mammals: *Plagiaulax* with cauliflower-like molars.

globe: they thus prepared the way for the penultimate conquest of
the world. The reproductive method of the Multituberculata is
also known, and it is quite comparable with that of modern
marsupials. In fact, although marsupials begin their development
as a fetus in the mother's uterus, they are attached to that organ
in a very precarious way: between the fetus and the uterine wall
the tissue known as the placenta, which is rich in blood vessels,
never appears. It is not therefore surprising that something like
an abortion results very soon after conception: the mother soon
expels the young, a miserable naked fetus, blind, inert and unconscious, and only an inch or so long. But the mother has a ventral
pouch, the well-known marsupial pouch which so greatly astonished the first zoologists to come face to face with Australian
animals. The young are immediately deposited in this pouch;
inside they attach themselves to the teats that hang there and a
veritable extra-uterine gestation begins. It lasts several weeks,
sometimes several months, before the young really comes into the

world, opens its eyes, puts out its head and, still continuing to
travel in its mother's pouch for a few more days, interests itself
in everything around, even beginning to browse on the lower
branches of trees while its mother feeds on the higher leaves.

Thus the first mammals passed through a marsupial stage. Then
the placenta appeared, and the Tertiary began some 70 million
years ago. Abruptly all the reptiles vanished from the surface of
the globe, except for a few species of lizards, turtles, serpents and
crocodiles. Then, also quite abruptly, the mammals made sensational progress: just like the reptiles that preceded them, they
came to occupy every kind of environment, so that not only
were there terrestrial mammals (the most numerous), but flying
mammals and marine mammals too. Moreover, they eventually
specialized in a number of different directions which, for simplicity's sake, can be reduced to three principal types. There were

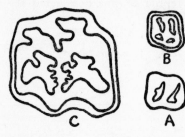

FIG. 92. The progressive complication of the grinding surfaces
of the molars of herbivores:
    A. *Phenacodus*;
    B. *Eohippus*;
    C. Modern horse.

the carnivores and the herbivores, each of these two main types
being characterized by acquiring means of attack or defence. While
the carnivores developed long and pointed canines, sharp molars
and paws with five toes and strong claws, the herbivores acquired
sharp incisors, molars for grinding and long slender feet that
assured safety in flight. The third specialization was distinguished
by the absence of any natural means of attack or defence, an
absence which was made good by the development of the brain,
whence followed the more or less systematic use of artificial instruments to assure the survival of the species: it is to this specialization that the Primates turned and found their consummation in
the appearance of the human species.

We must first study some typical examples of how these speciali-
zations occurred within the mammal class. The history of the
ancestors of the horse is classical. The first representatives were
small animals about the size of a fox, to which the name *Phenacodus*

FIG. 93. *Phenacodus,* the ancestor of numerous mammals.

is given: it had a long body, a pointed muzzle, a long tail and quite short limbs ending in five hoofed toes. Its teeth were still very simple, the molars being of medium height and bulk, furnished with two small crests of enamel of little importance. But it was from *Phenacodus* that all the branches of the great group of ungulates seem to have split off, that is to say the hoofed mammals: horses, rhinoceroses, elephants (pachyderms), pigs and boars, and finally the ruminants, with the five great families of Bovidae, Giraffidae, Camelidae, Cervidae and the Chevrotains.

With the passing of time—that is to say, throughout the 70 million years of the Tertiary—the ancestors of the horse progressively adapted themselves to running and to an herbivorous re-

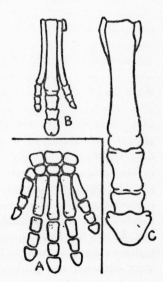

FIG. 94. Progressive reduction of the number of toes with adaptation to running in the ancestry of the horse.
    A. *Phenacodus;*
    B. *Mesohippus;*
    C. Modern horse.

gime. The short, thick-set, five-toed limbs of *Phenacodus* turned into the already slightly longer four-toed limbs of *Eohippus*, then into limbs with three toes (the central toe, the only one used in running, being prominent) of *Mesohippus*; finally only the very long toe of the modern horse survived, flanked at wrist level by two small rudimentary bony stylets, which still bear witness to the existence in its ancestors of three toes. While this evolution proceeded, the molars of *Phenacodus*, in the line of the horse, increased in height above the gum and also in bulk, at the same time as their grinding surfaces became complicated by the ap-

FIG. 95. *Mesohippus*, an ancestor of the horse.

pearance of crescents of enamel increasingly elaborate in outline.

One could similarly trace the evolution of teeth and feet which, from *Phenacodus*, leads either to the modern rhinoceros, or to the elephant, or to various types of ruminants or pigs.

It was from an animal undoubtedly very close to *Phenacodus* that the carnivores sprang. In this line we are faced with the abrupt replacement of hoofs by claws, while the evolution of the dental types is extremely typical. It is by following this evolution in the Felidae family—to which, besides the domestic cat, belong the lion, tiger, panther and jaguar—that we can best appreciate the characteristics of this dental specialization. The ancestors of the Felidae were small animals which must have strongly resembled our ferrets or skunks, with small and sharp incisors, pointed canines extending somewhat beyond the level of the molars, which were flattened and provided with sharp lengthwise crests. It was

then that appeared, at the beginning of the evolution of the carnivorous line, a special tooth which seemed intended to grind the
bones and to break the tendons. This tooth was the fourth pre-
molar in the upper jaw and the first of the large molars in the
lower jaw; it had a sharp edge followed by a flattened and enlarged heel and is called the carnassial.

From these small skunk-like carnivora there first arose some
larger carnivores, like *Nimravus* which, besides an already well
defined carnassial, showed canines that were beginning to lengthen,
especially in the upper jaw, while the size of the incisors was
diminishing. *Nimravus* was followed by animals of the genus
Felix, comparable to modern cats or lions, and then appeared two
species of tiger that have now vanished, of which the upper canines
were enormously lengthened and shaped like a dagger, while the

FIG. 96. Progressive reduction of the number of teeth, with
increase in the fangs of certain carnivores: A. *Smilodon:*
B. *Machairodus:* C. Lion: D. *Nimravus.* (After Romer.)

anterior crest of the carnassials was formidably sharp. These were
the *Machairodus* tiger and *Smilodon,* both contemporary with men
of the Reindeer Age. Deep grooves on either side of the lower
lip permitted the enormous fangs to pass; in attacking its prey the
animal used them like a dagger, as attested by the considerable
impression left on the skull by the muscles that moved the head.
It was by an abrupt movement of the neck that these tigers killed
their victims.

During this time, still deriving from small ancestors similar to
modern insectivora, flying mammals like bats, and marine mammals like dolphins, porpoises and whales, evolved and adapted themselves to an aerial medium and an aquatic medium respectively.
We are almost totally ignorant of the respective ancestors of these
two divergent lines of mammals.

*

Therefore, when the Tertiary began some 70 million years ago, the earth was occupied, so far as mammals are concerned, only by small animals with cauliflower-like molars, the Multituberculata, which were neighbours of other small marsupials strongly resembling our modern opossums. There were also present in very small numbers some forms of small size which already had a placenta, small shrew-mice without interesting specialization. But these animals are not the direct ancestors of any modern line; like many others, they were the "failures" of evolution that disappeared from the surface of the earth after a term that was fairly brief.

Then in various parts of the globe appeared several types of marsupials, some carnivorous and others herbivorous, all distin-

FIG. 97. *Brontops*, an attempt in the direction of the rhinoceros type.

guished by their very peculiar method of reproduction, that is to say, by the existence of the pouch inside which the young completed their development. But the marsupials were abruptly driven back to the periphery of the inhabited lands. Fifty million years ago they were only to be found in Australia, South America and South Africa. They were thrust aside by the sudden development— one is even tempted to speak of an evolutionary explosion—which produced the placental mammals.

Next began a warm period which lasted about 25 million years; during this time the earth was encircled by a wide equatorial zone, flanked to north and south by wide temperate zones. This was the epoch when, starting from *Phenacodus*, the principal ungulate split off. It was also the epoch when there came into being several types like the rhinoceros, with the North American Dinocerata,

FIG. 98. *Megacamelus:* an ancestor of the camel.

FIG. 99. *Alticamelus:* another ancestor of the camel.

about 10 feet high, with three pairs of horns, one on top of the head, one in front of the eyes and the third at the end of the snout. It was the epoch when the Titanotheres appeared in both North America and the Gobi Desert, as big as our elephants but built like our rhinoceros and possessing two great horns to right and left above the nostrils. Finally, this was the epoch when, in the marshes

FIG. 100. *Palaeomastodon:* one of the first elephants.

of Montmartre, Cuvier's *Anoplotherium* and *Palaeotherium* lived side by side, while among the carnivores there was a giant kind of skunk the size of a fox.

Next came the last part of the Tertiary; in about 20 million years the principal animal types that we know to-day came fairly rapidly into being. An American naturalist has said that if by chance a monumental Noah's Ark had preserved all the animals of this epoch, a child would have no hesitation in naming each of them, while its parents would think they were the victims of an hallucination, so surprised would they be by the abnormal size and appearance of these animals. A single example will illustrate this idea well: it is provided by the order of Proboscidea. All

FIG. 101. *Glyptodon:* a sort of giant armadillo.

animals of this order evolved in the direction of the elephant type. This was the moment when on the one hand there appeared the mastodons, giants with four tusks which, starting out from South Africa, progressively invaded Europe, crossed the Asiatic deserts and the Bering Straits, and reached the two Americas. During this time the more modest ancestors of our elephants remained in obscurity, but it was from them that the modern elephants and the gigantic mammoths that were contemporary with prehistoric man were born.

It was also at the end of the Tertiary that the ungulates with uneven numbers of toes—Artiodactyla—developed in a formidable way. Though until then they had been represented only by a few forms of which Oreodonta (ruminant pigs) was the most important, there was a sudden expansion, so that the ruminants to-

FIG. 102. *Megatherium*: a giant edentate
(toothless mammal).

day form the largest group of mammals. It was also at the end of
the Tertiary that giant Edentata developed in South America,
like *Glyptodon*, an armadillo-like creature, 11 feet 6 inches long, as
well as that huge species of bear, *Megatherium*, that had a long
prehensile tongue like our modern ant-eaters.

Finally, in the Tertiary, too, from those small insectivora resembling shrew-mice the primates split off, passing successively
through the types already described, the lemurians, the dog-faced
monkeys, the apes, then the anthropoids and finally man.

Part Three

THE WHY AND HOW OF THE
HISTORY OF LIFE

Megaceros, or Great Irish Deer, the contemporary of man's earliest ancestors.

The American *Mastodon*, an attempt in the direction of the elephant, dating from some millions of years ago.
(Paintings by C. R. Knight, Chicago Natural History Museum.)

A Jurassic landscape, about 200 million years ago.

(Piveteau: *Images des mondes disparus*)

CHAPTER VIII

The Indisputable Evolution of the Living World

HAVING reached this point, a pause is desirable, since the search for our ancestors must now be pursued in a rather different way. In their proper historical order, the first seven chapters have permitted us to show that in former times the earth was inhabited by vertebrates that to-day have vanished, and that it is possible to sketch the main branches of a genealogical tree from fishes to men. The question that remains concerns the roots of that tree, that is, what were the different stages which preceded the appearance of the first vertebrates on the surface of the earth, since traces of life can be found in the oldest rocks, dating from something like 1,500 million years ago, though the first fishes only made their appearance in the middle of the Primary, about 350 million years ago.

The great mass of invertebrates must now be noted, so that from their study we may deduce the main trends of life on earth that succeeded one another through the ages and found their end and blossoming in the large-brained primates. But it is important first of all to define, with the aid of the researches and techniques of study perfected during the last two centuries, how paleontology, stumbling upon the marine shells and petrified fishes, then discovering the great fossilized mammals and giant reptiles, permits us to close this history of life with a complete panorama of the sequence of the animal kingdom.

*

In simple terms the problem is as follows: since the main branches of the invertebrates were already differentiated at the time of the oldest legible rocks, a biological method must be found that will permit us to retrace by indirect methods the stages the invertebrate world passed in its evolution towards the vertebrate. This method is fully summed up in the very word "evolution." Until now it has only been implied, but not decisively demonstrated, that in both the animal and vegetable species there is a continuous line of derivation, the simple species giving rise to the more complex with the passing of time. This important biological proposition will soon have been in existence for two centuries, and in systematic use by zoologists and paleontologists for one century. Two French scholars and one English naturalist originated it.

*

Georges Louis Leclerc de Buffon, a Burgundian, was born at Montbard on September 7th, 1707, the son of a jurist and adviser to the Burgundy parliament. Brought up by Jesuits in Dijon, he continued his studies at the University of Angers. Throughout his youth he worked assiduously, but nothing in his tastes or reading yet suggested that he would one day devote himself to natural history. In fact, the only major event in his time at Angers that anyone has thought fit to reveal is that in a duel he had killed an officer with whom he had quarrelled. His earliest scientific inclinations were towards mathematics and physics, and it was he who translated into French the work in which Newton stated his theory of gravitation. Above all, it was at Angers that he formed a friendship with a young Englishman, Lord Kingston, who was visiting France with his tutor, Mr. Hickmann, an enthusiast for botany. So Buffon set off across France, Italy and England with his British friends. In their company he initiated himself a little into natural history, particularly on the plant side. It was in this capacity that in 1733, when he was 26, he was elected to the Academy of Science without having made any important scientific researches, which was quite the reverse to the case of Cuvier.

But shortly after he had finished his studies, he found himself in control of the large estate at Montbard, the most important place in the Côte d'Or. Very anxious for the prosperity of this inheritance from his mother, he set out to study the problems involved in the exploitation of its timber, the upkeep of the forests, the reproduction of young trees, the cutting, transport and preservation of the wood, and so on; but, being the owner of a few blast-furnaces, he improved his knowledge of chemistry and

geology at the same time, in order to acquire a proper understanding of ores and their extraction, as well as their metallurgical
treatment.

Undoubtedly it was in 1738 that occurred the decisive event in
Buffon's life, at the age of 31. On his deathbed Dufay, the physicist
and Intendant-General of the Jardin du Roy (that is, in fact,
Director of the Natural History Museum) named Buffon as his
successor, having been struck by the clarity of his scientific writings. Thus he became director of a botanical garden and obliged
by professional conscience to study botany and in a general way
all the natural sciences, for which, however, he was already prepared by his agricultural interests and by the botanizing expeditions he had made with Hickmann and his young English friend.
He carried these studies through quickly and with great keenness,
so that in 1749 he was in a position to publish the beginning of
his *Histoires naturelles,* a monumental work; its publication was
to continue for 50 years (though it was completed by his close
collaborators) and in it he undertook to describe completely all
the known species of the animal and vegetable kingdoms. From
various points of view it was one of the most important scientific
works of the eighteenth century. Its style was most elegant, and
despite some anachronisms it remains a very pleasant work to
read.

In 1753, simply for his literary style, Buffon was unanimously
elected to the Académie Française, without having to offer himself
as a candidate. This was the opportunity for him to deliver his
famous *Discours sur le style* at his admission, in which he insisted
on the necessity of presenting the most complex and serious ideas
in a clear, precise and elegant fashion.

So far as geology and paleontology are concerned, Buffon advanced some very sound ideas, cutting right across the opinions
prevalent at that time, and he appears as something more than a
forerunner; he is indeed an initiator of these sciences, and the
father of transformism too (better known as the theory of evolution), for he exercised a very great influence over Lamarck as well
as Cuvier. Buffon's ideas on the subject were never expressed as a
coherent whole: in general his works are rather confused and the
boldest propositions are mingled with the most pointless exercises
in style. The various works he published, or at least those that
were published under his direct inspiration, have to be studied

closely if his thoughts on the history of life are to be properly understood.

In his *Théorie de la terre* (1749), Buffon remarked upon the existence of fossilized shells embedded in the rocks and he did not hesitate a moment to regard them as the remains of marine animals that had vanished from those parts long ago. The idea was certainly not entirely new, since it had already been voiced several times, as far back as the days of Ancient Greece. But through Buffon this view at last received a place in natural science without arousing subsequent dispute.

*

One of Buffon's precursors was Bernard Palissy, a potter, who entered into legend because it is said that he burned his furniture in order to continue the firing of his pots. But Palissy was, above all else, a very great student of nature, and during numerous journeys through France, simultaneously practising glazing, portraiture and surveying, he concentrated his attention on natural objects, exploring caves, forests and quarries, and collecting shells with which he decorated what he himself called "rustic earthenware." But he used the shells that he found in beds of sandstone and chalk not only for the decoration of his pots; he preserved them in great numbers and made a valuable collection that formed a paleontological record of his native Saintonge, as well as of the Ardennes, Touraine and the Low Countries.

Thus, at the age of 65, in 1575, having collected fossil shells and petrified fishes from his earliest years, he ventured an opinion on their origin and significance. He had the courage to present these views to a Paris that was troubled with the "war of the three Henrys," in a series of lectures given between 1575 and 1584. Many scholars came to these talks, especially doctors and surgeons and the whole of the medical corps attached to the royal family. Palissy energetically declared that the shells and petrified fishes found embedded in the rocks were not by any means the natural freaks that they had until then been regarded; when a shell was found in a rock it was because in former times, very long ago, the shell-fish had been alive, but it had died when its receptacle had suddenly solidified. That is to say, before the existence of the marine world as we know it to-day, one or several marine worlds existed of which the most representative creatures have to-day disappeared. But despite the potter's convincing arguments and

the specimens he showed to support his statements, the doctors
of the Sorbonne systematically refused to admit the existence of
fossilized shells and fishes. They stuck to the simple and uncompromising explanation that they were natural freaks. Completely
ignored or misunderstood by his contemporaries, Palissy ended
his days in the Bastille in 1590, having been imprisoned for his
opinions at the age of 80 years.

However, this interpretation was not altogether new, for it had
already been maintained by a Dominican, Albert of Bollstadt,
300 years earlier. At Bollstadt in Swabia, north-east of the Lake of
Constance, was born in 1193 one of the most illustrious monks of
the Middle Ages. After his theological studies at Padua, he became Bishop of Ratisbon and ended by joining the order of
preaching friars founded by St. Dominic in 1215. He had already
shown himself very competent in natural philosophy—that is to
say, in the science of man and in physics and biology. In 1240 he
came to the Sorbonne. There is nothing surprising in the fact that
a foreigner, and particularly an ecclesiastic, should come to study
at one of the most famous universities in the whole world; later,
the Italian monk who eventually became St. Thomas Aquinas, did
the same thing. Latin was then the international language and it
was in Latin that the professors gave their lectures.

Albert of Bollstadt was most interested in reconciling the teachings of the scriptures with those of the Greek philosophers, handed
down by Byzantium to the Western Middle Ages through the
Arabic Near East. This concern was shared by St. Thomas Aquinas,
but the latter was more successful in effecting a reconciliation
between the Church and Greek paganism in a philosophy that
spread over the whole Christian world.

Albert of Bollstadt had a truly scientific mind: he began a
true classification of the sciences, defining each of them as far as
he was able, clearly showing the differences that must exist between mathematics, physics, biology and anthropology. Further,
probably for the first time since the advent of Christianity, he
insisted without equivocation on the necessity of observation and
experimentation; until then there was only too great a tendency
to accept revealed truth without taking the trouble to verify it.
It is in this respect that Albert of Bollstadt must be counted as one
of the leading scientific minds of the Middle Ages.

Applying himself especially to the study of what was not yet

known as paleontology, he had observed during the excursions
he made into the country that in the surroundings of Paris he
could collect very many stones in which animal remains were
embedded, the marine origin of which could not be doubted by
an experienced mind. He was thus led to recognize that these
were creatures that had lived in the oceans that had once occupied
the Paris area. They had been engulfed in the mud of the sea
bottom; then the earth and the water had mixed in such a way as
to cause a solidification in which the essential parts of the shell-fish
or its bones were preserved, the coldness and dryness of the stone
preventing putrefaction. Thus Albert of Bollstadt was forced to
admit that marine fauna once lived in regions now occupied by
the continents. Although his explanations might well be disputed,
they were nevertheless ingenious for the time, for he had discovered that certain animals had been "fossilized," that is to say
preserved, at least in their essential parts, inside the rocks long
after their deaths. He therefore had to admit that in former times
the fauna had not always been identical with modern fauna, and
by implication that the face of the earth had not remained unchanged since its creation.

This was an extremely daring position to take up at that time;
only one such as Albert, competent in all the sciences, could support it with valid arguments. By doing so, moreover, he made
the link with Aristotle, whose work he knew very well. What had
Aristotle to say about geology and paleontology? Thanks to his
personal observations and to the travellers' tales he was able to
collect from the mouths of his contemporaries (especially Herodotus, who had travelled much in Egypt), Aristotle had already
defined one of the essential facts of geology. For example, in the
mountains that flank the valley of the Nile on the west a very large
number of fossilized shell-fish are to be found, so that it is not
ridiculous to maintain that the whole of the Nile valley had at a
certain epoch been nothing but a gigantic gulf, a long and narrow
arm of the Mediterranean extending as far as Ethiopia. Later, this
arm of the sea had disappeared, giving place to the long valley
and to the delta through which the river now flows into the sea.
In other words, the respective situations of the sea and the continents had not been changeless throughout the ages: sometimes
the seas had covered the land, while at other times the seas had
receded, leaving fairly large parts of the continents dry.

What can we conclude from this? Simply, according to Albert of Bollstadt, and, through him, Aristotle—that it is possible to know the former appearance of the earth by studying the shells and petrified fishes to-day embedded in the rocks. Thus the essential principles of geology were laid down: the remains of vanished animals found in the rocks permit us to restore the fauna of former times: the study of the rocks themselves permit us to restore the landscapes and climates of those times. Finally, and above all, these observations decisively demonstrate that the history of the earth has been very varied and that several episodes followed one another, in which sometimes the seas and sometimes the dry land prevailed.

However, the teachings of Albert of Bollstadt, just like the vehement declarations of Palissy, were to remain a dead letter for a long time. Leonardo da Vinci, another universal mind, also considered that the shells found in the rocks were the remains of vanished animals. But the mind of the Middle Ages and the Renaissance was never aware that the earth had in former times shown a different face from that of to-day, that life on the earth could have been different from what it was in the sixteenth century. Meanwhile, an increasing number of amateurs began to take an interest in what were still considered to be freaks of nature: this was the epoch in which the first private collections were made that formed the origins of our museums. Of all these collections, one particularly deserves mention: that of Pope Sixtus V, which was studied and classified by Mercati, already mentioned at the beginning of this book in connection with his posthumous work, *Metallotheca Vaticana,* in which he discussed prehistoric flints. Nevertheless, Mercati was less successful in his study of the shells and petrified fishes, for he did not know how to make the comparison with existing species. This was the case also with Aldrovandi at the end of the sixteenth century, who possessed a very fine collection, the catalogue of which extended to 87 volumes all in the handwriting of the author. But he never expressed a rational opinion regarding these fossil remains: Aristotle, Albert of Bollstadt, Palissy and Leonardo da Vinci remained unrecognized forerunners. Nevertheless, they had seen things rightly: the surface of the earth had not always been peopled with animals like those before our eyes; the limits of the ocean and the dry land had not always been those that we now know.

✳

So Buffon brought these ideas concerning the past life of the earth to eventual triumph, and by his precise observations he laid the first foundations of geology and paleontology. Once again he demonstrated that in former ages, as evidenced by the fossilized shells, the seas had widely covered certain lands that to-day are dry. On the other hand he stressed the fact that certain animal forms now no longer exist: in support of this thesis he cited the famous ammonites, the cephalopods that flourished in the Secondary. Finally—still in his *Théorie de la terre*—Buffon clearly distinguished, among the fossilized shell-fish, between marine species of the open sea and others that were confined to the shore. It was therefore the essential base of the sciences of the earth (geology and paleontology) that Buffon discovered when he laid stress on the changes in the appearance of the earth through the ages in so far as the rocks, the flora and the fauna are concerned.

But Buffon went even further. In other works, especially in his *Epoques de la nature* (1778), he revealed the way in which the rocks were formed: the geological beds were deposited one upon the other during several thousands of years (this is the phenomenon now known to the geologists as stratification) and the study of these different beds should permit us to retrace the history of the earth and the history of life. Unfortunately, Buffon spent eight months of the year at his property at Montbard and four months at Paris superintending the Jardin du Roy, and never himself carried out any real practical work; he was unable to carry his theories concerning the history of the earth to their conclusion. However, it is clear that for the age in which he was writing he took an extremely daring stand in both geological and biological matters.

What seems to have been his most revolutionary stand is that by which he disagreed that the superimposed geological beds were laid down during the 40 days of the Flood: he maintained that it took thousands and thousands of years to form these sedimentary rocks, and this led him into giving the earth an age of at least 75,000 years and into dividing the history of the earth into six successive epochs. These ideas were not very well received by his contemporaries and for the sake of peace Buffon had to compromise a little with the ecclesiastical authorities, without however making any large concessions. As to the laity, who were astonished by the figure he gave, he answered them substantially in this way: "Why does it seem to you more difficult to reckon 100,000 years than to reckon 100,000 pounds in money?" The estimate was not a casual one; Buffon had made his calculations and the following quotation from his *Epoques de la nature* still remains, by its clarity and elegance of style, one of the best demonstrations possible of the methods which were long used by geologists for calculating the age of the fossil beds:

"To make it easier to appreciate this idea, let us take an example: let us find out how long it took to construct a hill of clay 1,000 toises [1] high. The successive sediments of the waters formed all the beds of which the hill is composed from base to summit. Now, we can judge the successive daily deposits of the water by the thin layers of clay; they are so thin that a dozen can be counted within the thickness of a line. Let us therefore suppose that each tide deposits a sediment one-twelfth of a line thick, that is to say one-sixth of a line each day; the deposit will increase by one line in six days, by six lines in 36 days and therefore by something like 5 inches a year, which gives us more than 14,000 years as the time required for the formation of a hill of clay 1,000 toises high."

Finally, applying himself to the study of fossil types, Buffon clearly established that in the course of ages certain forms had been replaced by others and he stressed that "the less perfect species, those that were more delicate, heavier, less active or less well armed have already vanished or will vanish with time." In this little phrase, Buffon had quite simply laid the basis of modern transformism which Lamarck and Darwin brought to success; it summarizes in a few words what his book has dealt with in its first 200 pages. Thus, when he died in Paris on April 10th, 1788, aged 81 years, he had laid the first foundations of the natural sciences which were to make such fine progress during the nineteenth and twentieth centuries.

Then, at the beginning of the nineteenth century, very different from one another in their scientific opinions, in their careers and their relations with their contemporaries, came Lamarck and Cuvier, Darwin and Saint-Hilaire: three Frenchmen and one Englishman, four contrary temperaments, four pioneers of zoology, biology and paleontology.

Jean Baptiste de Monet, Chevalier de Lamarck, was born at Bazantin on the Somme on August 1st, 1744. Though he was

[1] One toise = 1.78 metres = 5 feet 10 inches.

not in the least attracted to an ecclesiastical career, he entered a
seminary in response to his father's wish; but on the death of his
father the young Lamarck, aged 17 years, fled from the Jesuits and
joined the armies of Louis XV. Shortly afterwards he was obliged
to leave the army as the result of a wound. Without resources, but
not at all discouraged, he went to seek his fortune in Paris, and in
order to live eventually found work in a bank; articles which he
sent to various journals assured him the means to live a decent life.
But the Chevalier de Lamarck was anxious above all to attend
lectures and discussions, and to be able to pay for books and
concert seats. Indeed, it was rather a self-taught mind that sought
to learn everything and to know everything in all fields of human
thought. Perhaps it is rightly reserved to intelligences of this kind
to elaborate scientific or philosophical syntheses more vigorous
—and because they always stray a little from officially recognized
facts, more daring, too—than those produced by minds that stick
closer to the strict observance of facts, and facts alone, which
eventually hold them in bondage. This is the moment to point out
the contrast between Cuvier and Lamarck, although the comparison should be even more fruitful when Lamarck's views on
paleontology have been clearly defined.

During his first 10 years in Paris, from 1766 to 1776, Lamarck
certainly seems to have touched upon almost everything without
settling anywhere. He was a musician with an enthusiasm for
medicine, a botanist with an interest in methods of weather fore-
casting, who moreover published several *Annuaires météorologiques*
at the end of his career. But it was botany that eventually held his
attention and his assiduousness brought him the friendship of old
Bernard de Jussieu, creator of the Trianon gardens. For Bernard
de Jussieu botany was the only subject worthy of study, and when
he died at the age of 78 years, despite royal favours, he was still
what he had been all his life, a simple botany demonstrator at the
Jardin du Roy, a modest position which he took on so as to be
able to work in peace. Lamarck was indebted to him for the opportunity to learn theoretical and practical botany during the
many botanical excursions they made together, in which they were
sometimes joined by Jean Jacques Rousseau.

It is not surprising that in 1778 Lamarck was in a position to
publish a *Flore générale de la France*, a noteworthy book that at
once went through two editions, with a third edition in 1802; it

was warmly received by the director of the future museum, Buffon. The latter soon appointed Lamarck as Correspondent of the Jardin du Roy, which permitted him to go abroad to continue his botanical studies, notably in Germany and Austria, together with Buffon's son. Lamarck's career was settled from that time on. Returning to France in 1790, he became librarian at the Natural History Museum, a post which he held for four years. At that moment the Convention, which was completely reorganizing higher education in France, decided to give the botanist a chair for which no candidate seemed worthy of interest—the chair in invertebrate zoology. With remarkable courage, at the age of 50 years, Lamarck undertook the study of the invertebrates about which he had now to teach his pupils. Between 1815 and 1822 he published seven volumes on the *Histoire naturelle des animaux sans vertèbres*. Yet he remained the best botanist of the Revolution and the Empire, and his *Histoire générale des végétaux* published between 1802 and 1826 in collaboration with Brisseau de Mirbel, another eminent botanist, was for a long time an authoritative work.

But Lamarck's vital work, certainly more theoretical than practical, had sensational repercussions; it was that which dealt with the relations between living creatures and their evolution on the surface of the earth: the *Recherches sur l'organisation des corps vivants* (1800). Two main ideas, very different from one another, are contained in this work; they must not be confused, because one of them has retained almost all its value for 150 years, while the other, which only aimed at providing a rational explanation of the first, can no longer be maintained, at least not in its original form.

On the one hand, and probably because he had especially studied plants and invertebrate animals, Lamarck claimed that all species derived one from another, the more simple having given rise to the more complex, following progressive anatomical and physiological changes which had lasted for thousands and thousands of years. Essentially this was an idea of Buffon's, which Lamarck took over, expounding it perhaps more clearly and more explicitly. But in expressing his thoughts without equivocation, he must truly be regarded as the father of transformism or, as we say to-day, of evolution. It was to him that nineteenth-century authors referred when they finally accepted this doctrine.

What exactly is meant when we speak of the theory of evolution? Simply, that the study of the remains of animals that have now vanished from the surface of the globe shows a continuous chain: that the history of life has progressed from the simple to the complex, passing from single-celled creatures to the exceedingly complicated mammals; that throughout the ages, for the thousands of millions of years since the earth separated from the sun, the animal species, and also the plant species, differentiated, became complicated and increasingly better fitted to lead autonomous lives. Some examples of this have already been given in the preceding studies of the zoological groups most familiar to the lay public: amphibians sprang from certain fish, reptiles sprang from amphibians, and in their turn the mammals sprang from certain reptilian stocks, as did the birds too. Such successions are proved to-day with the aid of many arguments calling upon many branches of natural science. Two of the most typical of these arguments can be mentioned here. The groups just referred to appear one after the other in the history of the earth, the mammals being younger than the reptiles, which are younger than the amphibians, which are younger than the fishes: this is the paleontological argument. On the other hand, in the last 20 years there has been no end to the discovery of what are called missing links, that is to say intermediate and composite creatures, simultaneously uniting the characteristics of two neighbouring groups, as is the case with the Coelacanth, the ape-men of South Africa or the man-apes of Java and China, and also the series of Siberian and South African fossil reptiles which provide the link between the reptiles and the mammals. So much for the anatomical argument.

One could go further still and seek even more convincing proofs by reference to embryology, which reveals the resemblances between larval forms of which the adults seem zoologically quite separated one from the other, by reference to the study of blood groups when possible, and by reference to studies of the hereditary transmission of certain characteristics.

One of the best demonstrations in support of evolution seems to have been presented a few years ago by Father de Saint-Seine, a well-known French paleontologist. He confined himself to various examples, that of the Coelacanth in particular and a strange fossil amphibian from Madagascar. Professor Jean Piveteau of Paris made this *Protobatrachus* known in 1937; it shows certain features of our modern frogs and toads—the lymphatic system, the essential structure of which can be deduced after the manner of certain vertebrates, and certain other characteristics typical of very primitive amphibians, like the absence of the urostyle which assures the maximum efficacy in leaping movements whether on terra firma or in swimming. Furthermore, the ankle bones of *Protobatrachus* are rather elongated, not quite as much as in modern frogs and toads but much more than in salamanders. Once again, this is an intermediate animal, of a form that shows the means by which the transition from the primitive amphibians, deriving from the fish with lungs, into the very specialized

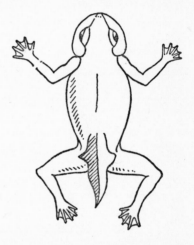

FIG. 103. Reconstruction of
Protobatrachus.

amphibians of the modern world, was made. Now, knowing the laws of paleontology and accepting the theory of evolution, one could foresee that such an intermediate form should be found— if at all—in Triassic rocks dating from 200 to 150 million years ago: in fact, the already clearly distinguished Salentia date from the end of the Triassic, while the non-specialized amphibians, likely to have given rise to such forms, are found in the Permian rocks. It was precisely in the Triassic rocks of Madagascar that *Protobatrachus* was found. Once more, as Father de Sainte-Seine picturesquely says, the fossil was found at the estimated rendezvous. Can a better indirect proof or neater demonstration in support of evolution be conceived?

*

None of this is far removed from Lamarck, since for 150 years zoology and paleontology have only brought grist to the mill he set in motion. Certainly, several attempts have been made to bury transformism. One of the most convincing—and most honest— of its adversaries was Vialleton, a Genevese anatomist of repute at the beginning of this century; his arguments are to-day largely superseded.

Lamarck had few admirers and left no direct disciples. He ended his life almost in poverty, abandoned by his fellows and living on a modest pension; moreover, he became blind, probably through the daily use of a magnifying glass while examining plants and invertebrate animals. He presented transformism clearly for the first time, but he died unrecognized, overwhelmed by the glory of his rival Cuvier, who was nevertheless his colleague.

Before presenting Lamarck's second thesis concerning the working of evolution in living creatures, it will be interesting to bring the diametrically opposed opinions of Cuvier and Lamarck face to face. Cuvier was an impenitent and intransigent believer in the fixity of species. For him the different animal species were created independently of one another, without any connection whatever between them. The earth changed its face several times— six times to be exact—and earlier types of fauna were replaced by new and different fauna; the disappearances were the work of cataclysms affecting the entire planet, following which the new fauna arose from nothing and so peopled the globe. The paleontologist should simply study these fauna and flora as six independent blocks, separated from one another by "revolutions."

What could Lamarck the transformist do against such peremptory statements? He was an unobtrusive person, neither very talkative nor demonstrative, and not very brilliant in company; although he enjoyed a certain fame as a botanist, he was at most regarded as a conscientious professor whose work had scarcely a chance of passing to posterity. Moreover, it must be admitted that Lamarck sometimes took it into his head to leave his own field for those of chemistry, physics and meteorology, which was a catastrophe, since the ideas he defended in these fields a little more than a century ago now deserve a place only in a joke book. Finally, to read his *Philosophie zoologique*, with its confusion of ideas and feeble style, unredeemed by the elegance that we find in Buffon, is to be convinced that such an amateur had no chance of interesting minds under the spell of Cuvier. That is why both France and Europe were ignorant of transformism for many years. Almost alone, Charles Lyell, the greatest British geologist of the nineteenth century and the one who went to Abbeville in 1859 to support Boucher de Perthes, revived and confirmed (at least in their general outline) the fundamental ideas that Lamarck had published in his *Principes de géologie* in 1830. The question may certainly be raised as to how French geologists and paleontologists at the beginning of this century would have come to know the works of their colleagues but for the existence of Charles Lyell on the other side of the Channel.

However, in France itself the transformist dispute had something of an echo when, in 1830, at a memorable meeting of the Academy of Science, it brought the two friends, Cuvier and Etienne Geoffroy Saint-Hilaire, into opposition. Saint-Hilaire, a talented zoologist, had been teaching at the National History Museum since 1784 and for the first time in France conducted a course on birds and mammals. When he had secured this post at the age of 22 years, he made Georges Cuvier (his senior by three years) come to Paris the next year to occupy a post at the Ecole Centrale du Panthéon. These two followed brilliant careers on parallel lines. But Saint-Hilaire soon conceived an idea that he took very much to heart; it was his theory of a general plan of the organization of living creatures. He maintained, often in the face of a certain amount of abuse, that all animals are constructed on the same lines and that all their parts—comparing, for example, a horse and an octopus—should be capable of being related one to another. This was no more nor less than a transformist thesis, stated in a different form and with less precision than Lamarck, since this pre-established plan assumed a close relationship between the species, quite the contrary of the successive and independent creations conceived by Cuvier. This was the origin of the famous squabble between the two friends in 1836, especially as Saint-Hilaire had some sympathy for Lamarck's ideas. An impassioned dispute began that was, however, always courteous and friendly; a synthesis rich in future discoveries could perhaps have emerged from it but for the death of Cuvier shortly afterwards, in 1832. Two different types of mentality had clashed; Cuvier showed respect for facts while Saint-Hilaire defended the right of hypothesis. But it was finally this right of hypothesis that swept Cuvier away when, in the last decades of the nineteenth century, transformism made its official entry into science. It returned from England in the works of Charles Darwin who, like Lamarck, besides his final achievement in bringing the idea of the evolution of the living world to success, applied himself to giving it a rational explanation.

If the history of antiquity had had to reckon with Cleopatra's nose, the history of science, 2,000 years later, had very nearly to reckon with Darwin's nose when, with a warm recommendation from Henslow, the 22-year-old Charles Darwin presented himself to Captain Fitz-Roy the commander of the *Beagle*, who was preparing to make a voyage round the world and looking for a naturalist to go with him. Now, Fitz-Roy claimed to be an expert in physiognomy: young Darwin's nose showed signs of such lack of energy that he was very nearly left behind. Nevertheless, he was accepted at the last minute and in December 1831 the *Beagle* got under way for a five-year voyage. Without this voyage who would dare to say that transformism would have known such success and that the publication in 1859 of Darwin's *Origin of Species*, exactly 50 years after Lamarck's *Philosophie zoologique*, would have marked one of the crucial dates in the history of biology?

Charles Darwin's childhood had not been exemplary. Born on February 12th, 1809, this grandson of Erasmus Darwin, one of the greatest English biologists of the eighteenth century, and son of Robert Darwin, one of the best-known doctors in Shropshire, had been a very inattentive scholar. Scarcely anything mattered to him except birds'-nesting or pinning out butterflies, unless it was gathering shells on the sea-shore or medicinal plants for pressing or drying in his herbarium. He thus showed a much developed taste for the natural sciences in the extremely practical way of the English, in the appreciation of the bursting of the buds in spring and the ripening of the fruits in autumn, in the study of the best way to recognize a tree in winter by its stature and its bark, or the best way to identify a bird or a small rodent at 30 yards or to follow the daily growth of a plant or the germination of an acorn or beech-nut. This is in fact a particularly British taste.

The young Darwin thought he would be able to satisfy this love of nature by undertaking the study of medicine; but he soon abandoned the project when as a young probationer he was present at a surgical operation which left him half fainting. He then decided to turn to an ecclesiastical career and when he was 19 entered Cambridge University; there he formed a friendship with the botanist, Professor Henslow who, by the daily example he set, both in the practical field of botanical observation and in the field of scientific criticism, greatly contributed to shaping the mind of Charles Darwin.

From the voyage of the *Beagle* he returned to Europe in 1836, and until his death in 1882 he devoted himself with equal success to the most minute botanical and zoological researches (e.g. the monographs on barnacles, the fertilization of orchids, insectivorous plants) and to the most daring biological syntheses (*The Origin of Species*, 1859; *The Descent of Man*, 1870).

It is impossible in a few pages to summarize the ample harvest of scientific observation which Darwin brought back from his voyage in October 1836, when he was 27 years old. It is sufficient to summarize the principal facts that he himself brought to notice. Of these facts two deserve special emphasis: the exhumation in South America of skeletons of giant armadillos that have now vanished, so like modern armadillos that Darwin at once concluded that the modern armadillos were the direct descendants of very old extinct forms. This was a revival of Lamarck's transformist ideas—with which he was familiar, for throughout the expedition his bedside book had been Lyell's *Principles of Geology*. But now it was more convincing, for it was easier to influence scientific opinion that had been freed from its quasi-religious respect for Cuvier and shaken by the publications of Lyell, Boucher de Perthes and Albert Gaudry.

The other fact that had struck Darwin forcibly was the distribution of tortoises in the Galapagos Islands of the Pacific Ocean, off the South American coast. On each of the six islands which form this archipelago there lived a species of giant tortoise reaching to 3 or even 6 feet in length. All these tortoises had an indisputable family likeness, so that one might regard them all as of the same genus. But each island had its own different species, as if, isolated when the islands separated one from another, and starting from the same primitive giant type, several secondary types of tortoise became clear in a few million years. This once more proved that animal types are capable of transforming themselves and that the animal species are not unchanging.

But Darwin went further. He brought back from his voyage

many observations that permitted him not only to demonstrate the reality of evolution but also to account for the biological phenomena that caused it. This is the moment to contrast the Lamarckian and Darwinian theories concerning the inner workings of transformism and to present a short synthesis of modern ideas on the subject. For in recent years an American paleontologist, George G. Simpson, has published a long and very difficult study of the problem from which one is reasonably justified in expecting a clarification of speculative paleontology.

A complete analysis cannot be made here, but we may state the question clearly in the way it faced the author himself. George Simpson is a paleontologist, that is to say he has been led throughout his career to concentrate on fossils with the object of describing them, of placing them in their true (?) position in the classification of living creatures and, on a higher plane but also a more "public" one, to face the problem of the relationships of living creatures that have vanished with one another, and also between them and modern creatures. But to study evolution, the existence of which, for any real scientific significance, cannot be doubted, is automatically to raise the question of the mechanism of evolution. Darwin answered the question in an authoritative way, by urging the importance of natural selection or, as is often said, the struggle for existence; he thus took up a position diametrically opposed to that of Lamarck, who gave priority as a factor in evolution to the influence of environment. We can illustrate these two positions very shortly by means of the two following illustrations.

If, for example, it is a question of explaining why the giraffe has a long neck, this is how Darwin and Lamarck differ. Lamarck explained that the giraffe formerly lived in places where the only food accessible in great quantity consisted of the leaves of very high trees. To reach these high leaves the giraffes had to stretch their necks; so, from generation to generation, their necks grew longer. But, according to Darwin, among the "pre-giraffes" with fairly short necks there were some slight variations: some pre-giraffes had necks slightly longer than had others, just as some men have arms slightly longer than their fellows. But the giraffes with slightly longer necks were able to feed better, had a better chance of surviving and reproducing their kind than those with shorter necks; so, progressively, the giraffe's neck attained its present length.

To summarize these slightly over-simplified theories, it may be said that according to Lamarck the giraffe stretched its own neck in order to reach higher, while according to Darwin the modern giraffe has a long neck because it gradually eliminated his shorter-necked congeners.

So Simpson, by way of his researches, came face to face with the problem of the appearance of new characteristics. Furthermore, he had to try and solve the problem of the hereditary transmission of acquired characteristics, a problem that Lamarck and Darwin regarded as solved.

But other scientists too have faced the problem of the hereditary transmission of characteristics: they were the geneticists who in 1900 rediscovered the Mendelian laws. The strides made by genetics in these last 50 years can only be compared with those made by nuclear physics; genetics has overtaken, if not surpassed, paleontology, which has more than 200 years of long and difficult research behind it. Now it is an incredible fact that paleontologists and geneticists have until recently systematically ignored one another. The geneticists, and more generally the biologists, have become neo-Darwinians, maintaining the primordial importance of the "struggle for existence" as the motive element in evolution; the paleontologists, often without admitting it frankly, insist on the influence of environment.

The biologist is interested in discussing what happens to 100 rats in the course of 10 years under single given conditions, while the paleontologist has to ask himself what has happened to 1,000 million rats in the course of 10 million years in the fluctuating conditions of the history of the earth.

In 30 generations of rats only modifications of small importance are observed: the rats still remain rats, they simply change colour or become susceptible to this or that cancer or organism, and at the most they lose or gain a digit on a given foot. On the other hand, in 30 million generations, if one can carry out such a study on all the rats in nature, it is more than probable that one would see them change into another genus of rodents, or even quite simply become extinct, giving place to another animal family. This, in rough form, according to Simpson, is the grounds for the divorce between the paleontologists and the geneticists.

Now Simpson has attempted what is really a preliminary to reconciliation. Judge and party to the case, he brings the geneticist and the paleontologist together. What, he asks, is a geneticist? He is one who shuts himself up in a room, draws the curtains, watches small flies frisking about in a flask and thinks he is studying nature. The paleontologist? One who undertakes to study the principle of internal combustion engines by standing at the corner of the street to watch passing cars. Such is the amusing way the American scientist has described the complaints of the parties that face one another. Yet the two branches of science must settle the problem of the evolution of the species, since this problem comes back in the end to knowing the mechanism by which hereditary characteristics appear and are transmitted. In this matter, therefore, Simpson has brought about a veritable revolution. To the geneticists who know only one aspect of the problem (the 30 generations of rats aspect) an expert has brought the viewpoint of 30 millions of rats. This viewpoint is extremely complex and varied, although in simplifying it in the extreme, it must be admitted that Simpson remains a neo-Darwinian. What he proposes to the paleontologists throughout his work is rather a new line of research than a new theory of evolution.

But it is naturally impossible, without straying beyond the framework of this work, which has simply to retrace the principal stages in the history of life, to dwell long on the inner determinism of evolution. One can only speak of it briefly, to satisfy a very justifiable curiosity on the part of the reader. Moreover, it would be better to leave the neo-Darwinians and the neo-Lamarckians face to face for a few more years, to be patient in our curiosity and await the more satisfying explanations which the collaboration of the geneticists and paleontologists will soon give. It will suffice for the moment that the proofs brought to the support of transformism may be sufficiently convincing to justify this history and to provide a method that will permit the study of the first stages through which life passed between its appearance on the earth and the differentiation of the first vertebrates.

CHAPTER IX

Life, the Queen of the Seas

THE history of life, and therefore the erratic path that man has followed in search of his ancestors, is not yet ended. It is all very well to have traced the general outline of the vertebrate branch but, when the paleontologist has identified the most primitive fishes, he has not even then definitely revealed the deepest roots of living creatures.

Long before Cuvier, throughout the period covered by Albert of Bollstadt, Palissy, Leonardo da Vinci and Aldrovandi, the fossilized shell-fish and fishes had been identified, but often without fully understanding their general significance. It was seen that life had come into being in the sea and after much discussion, many hesitations and controversies, the paleontologists returned in the end to the propositions of the Greek philosopher Anaximander, that were later revived by several writers of the Middle Ages and the Renaissance in the more compact form, *Omne vivum ex aqua* (every living creature comes from the water). The first fishes having made their appearance towards the middle of the Primary era, it is therefore to the Pre-Cambrian, Cambrian and Silurian seas that we must turn in order to discover the stages crossed by life before the vertebrate stage was reached. The search is very disappointing.

*

Take, for example, the face of the earth more than 1,000 million years ago. We can know it by studying the Pre-Cambrian rocks. But unfortunately these rocks have been reformed several times in the course of the ages; thrust deep into the bosom of the earth under the pressure of marine sediments which have been deposited on their surface for 1,500 million years, they have been so compressed and raised to such a temperature that the principal mineral elements contained in them have melted, then recrystallized when movements of the earth's crust have cooled them again by thrusting them up towards the surface. These are known as "metamorphic" rocks, although a strict definition of metamorphism cannot be given here, for it is a complex phenomenon and all geologists are not agreed about its inner mechanism. Anyway, the animal remains contained in the rocks that have been subjected to metamorphism have in their turn been so heated and compressed that they are rare and often fragmentary. Despite all this, it has been possible to reconstruct in a rough way what could have been the appearance of the earth at this distant epoch and what could have been the fauna that lived in it.

The dry land formed four large continental shelves, on which the sediments settled as relatively light beds or beds that have been raised at a recent epoch in the history of life, in such a way that one can still make geological explorations in them to-day. These old continental shelves are known as shields. They are: the North Atlantic shield (comprising Canada and the northern part of the United States, and also Greenland, which was separated from Canada in the Pre-Cambrian era by a long and narrow arm of the sea), the Baltic shield (corresponding to Sweden, Finland and the north-western part of Russia), the Saharan shield (covering the greater part of modern Africa), and finally the Brazilian shield (corresponding to the eastern shoulder of South America). In some parts of Canada the Pre-Cambrian rocks are found at the surface; elsewhere, they are buried deep in the earth, and in North America, for example, it is at the very bottom of the gigantic gash of the Colorado canyon that they are to be found. In general, the boundaries of these ancient shelves are clearly outlined on the map by the existence of a chain of lakes situated one behind the other and connected by water-courses. In North America it is the almost continuous chain of the Bear Lake, the Slave Lake, then the frontier lakes of the United States (Superior, Michigan, Huron, Erie and Ontario, the last two being separated by the Niagara falls). In Northern Europe we have the Finnish lakes Ladoga and Onega, then all the little lakes that roughly correspond to the frontier between Norway and Sweden. It is to the north of them that, in the oldest rocks in the world, the remains of a very varied fauna are found, already very complex since, after a fashion and despite the mutilation they have undergone, the existence of molluscs, crustaceans and worms can be observed, that is to say widely differentiated types of zoological organization.

When we take a look at the surface of the earth several million years later our observations are even more disappointing. In fact, at the beginning of the Primary, a walk along the Cambrian and Silurian shores would not disclose a strange world; not very much could be learned about the evolution of life before the appearance of the first vertebrates, that is to say the first fishes, the jaw-less Ostracoderms of the end of the Silurian, about 350 million years ago. But for 700 to 1,000 million years, very many invertebrates, very varied in form, had already preceded them and, however far one goes into the past, these already widely differentiated inverte-brate types are familiar. Furthermore, despite a certain number of invertebrates that are interesting in the strangeness of their forms or in their abnormal size, all these types tell the paleontologist very little, for they scarcely differ from types existing to-day.

The sponges and jelly-fish and (very numerous in some tropi-cal seas) the coral-forming polyps, madrepores and coralloids, were already there. Then, fixed to the rocks or spread over the shells or carapaces of other marine creatures, were colonies of Bryozoa, some in the form of minute trees and others like wrinkled and irregular plates; these creatures, although generally ignored because of their small size, are very abundant in most of the seas to-day, just as they were in the Primary seas. These colonies of Bryozoa are formed from very small sac-shaped individuals, but more complicated than the hydras and polyps, secreting a small protective shell made of lime or of that organic matter called chitin, which forms the external covering of insects. The tiny individuals join together into an encrusting or bush-like colony.

The shellfish were there, too: all the molluscs—the gastropods, with their houses on their backs, and the lamelli-branchs, roughly reminiscent of our oysters, mussels and scallops, although there were some giant forms with shells more than 3 feet across—and, above all, the cephalopods, though our octopuses and cuttle-fishes can give no idea of the variety and paleontological importance of this group during the Primary and Secondary eras. We have already spoken of the spiral creatures known as ammonites, which literally filled the seas of the Secondary.

There were two strange types of crustaceans, the trilobites and the Gigantostraca (also known as Eurypterida), both covered, as our crustaceans still are, by a carapace of chitin entirely or partly divided into rings. The trilobites owe their names to their external appearance, which is divided into three main parts: a "head" more or less flat and covered with a one-piece carapace; then an abdomen, broken up into rings of varying width and length according to the species, comparable to what is almost the "tail" of our shrimps and crayfish; and finally a tail, called the telson, flat and flanked with blades functioning simultaneously as fins and elevators, but atrophied in almost all species. The majority of trilobites were of modest size, from an inch or so to the size of the hand, but there were also giant forms, one of them attaining a length of nearly 5 feet. These crustaceans, so typical of the Primary seas, moved upon the bottom and occasionally buried themselves in the mud, feeding on small animal prey and small molluscs, and browsing on the algae.

The Gigantostraca, which easily reached to 6 feet long, had heads protected by a flat carapace that extended into a long "tail," segmented or not, and a pointed telson. They seem to have been formidably carnivorous and to have competed in some degree with the armoured fish in the seas of the late Primary.

Finally there were the marine worms, sea-urchins and starfish, while the first insects, a kind of giant dragon-fly, began to fly about the Carboniferous forests.

This is a very rapid panorama of marine life for more than 500 million years. But there is no question here of a treatise on paleontology, and even less of making an exhaustive list of all the invertebrate species that inhabited our planet in former ages. To present the various forms of invertebrates, it would be necessary to give a long description of each one of about ten main types, and to provide a new vocabulary, with adequate definitions. This is something that can safely be ignored as of use only to the expert, but there is no question of passing over in silence the general succession of living creatures that take us from microscopic forms to man.

*

The simplest way to an understanding of the essential basis of zoological classification still depends on embryological studies. Whether in the animal or vegetable species, reproduction always results (with few exceptions, which confirm the rule!) from the union of a male element, called the sperm, and a female element, called the ovum. The union of these two microscopic elements is called fertilization. The fertilized ovum divides up rapidly to give two daughter cells, and each of these daughter-cells itself divides and forms two daughters, and so on, quickly developing into a small sphere of some hundreds of cells. Soon, following embryological processes which vary with every species, the cells draw apart to form a hollow sphere called the blastula. At a later stage it is found that the cells of the blastula, all identical until then, split up into two different types: by the phenomenon of gastrulation, some of the cells that form the wall of the sphere penetrate to its interior, so that a small cellular canal now runs down to the bottom of the sphere with a small orifice at its surface. Gastrulation thus ends in the separation of the embryo into an external cellular wall, called the ectoderm, and a sort of glove-finger that hangs into the interior of the sphere, called the endoderm. In other words, in its gastrula stage the embryo has the appearance of a double-walled sac.

There are some animals that remain more or less at this stage of embryological development: sponges, medusas and polyps, or to put it more scientifically, the Spongiae and the Coelenterata. Some fairly large cells form the external layer of the gastrula;

The egg, a single cell

changes into a hollow blastula

then into a gastrula in which ectoderm and endoderm are individualised

and in which the mesoderm soon appears

Fig. 104.

they play a protective role and in the Coelenterata sometimes give
rise either to tentacles (certain medusas, sea anemones, freshwater
hydras, etc.) or to minute organs of defence that throw out a spike,
barbed with tiny spines, at its prey or enemy; these cells, that
secrete a venomous liquid that stings like the liquid elaborated by
the leaves of nettles (it is moreover a matter of common experience that medusas—or jelly-fish—stranded on our beaches can
cause quite painful if not dangerous burns), are called nematocysts
and are characteristic of the Coelenterata. Then there are the small
cells that form the inner wall of the sac: they play an essential role
in the digestion of the prey captured by the tentacles or the
nematocysts. Thus, ignoring certain structural details of little
importance here, the medusas and sea anemones are the simplest
of all animals: they are double-walled sacs, the ectoderm playing
a protective role and the endoderm a digestive role. During their
embryological development the majority of invertebrates and all
the vertebrates pass through such a stage: at a certain moment in
their lives they are nothing more than two differential layers of
cells and are therefore diploblastic animals. However, it would be
a mistake to try and put the Coelenterata at the origin of the
animal branch, for certain peculiarities of their structure reveal
that they are already fairly specialized in certain directions, as
witnessed by the appearance of stinging cells and of cells specialized
in receiving messages from the external world, that is to say cells
that behave more or less like nervous cells.

But this first outline of zoological classification permits us to
make a clear contrast between the diploblastic animals (Spongiae
and Coelenterata) and all other animals, which continue their
embryological development by acquiring a third layer. In fact,
at the moment of gastrulation or soon after it is finished, certain
cells, some originating from the ectoderm, some from the endoderm, and some from these two simultaneously, come to form
small cellular masses which spread in the cavity between the glove-
finger and the outer wall. To this third cellular group the name
mesoderm has been given because of its intermediate position.
The embryo has thus become triploblastic; it will give rise to
triploblastic animals, that is to say all invertebrates and all vertebrates with the exception, once again, of the Spongiae and the
Coelenterata.

The larva thus formed evolves progressively towards the adult type. The ectoderm differentiates so as to produce both the external covering of the body and the nervous system; from the endoderm originate all the organs of the digestive tract and, in the vertebrates, the pulmonary apparatus too; finally, from the mesoderm develop the organs of excretion, the muscles, the blood and most of the skeleton, where there is one. The triploblastic animals have pursued two parallel evolutionary lines, characterized by a progressive complication of the anatomical organization and physiological functioning. The zoologists and paleontologists easily distinguish between these two lines by studying the position of the nervous system in relation to the digestive tract. In the majority of the invertebrates the nervous system is always in a ventral position below the digestive tract: this structure is characteristic of the hyponeural line, in which are found the principal types of invertebrate organization in the modern world, as well as the marine and terrestrial worms (leeches, earthworms, many marine worms like the lug-worm, etc.), the molluscs, crustaceans, insects and arachnids. It is with the insects that the hyponeural line seems to have reached its maximum evolutive capacity.

On the other hand, the epineural line in which the nervous system is in a dorsal position, stretching along the body above the digestive tract, is more interesting to consider since it ends in man. The first epineural creatures known to us were the graptolites, all of them fossilized. They appear to have had a trunk bearing on all sides small beads like hollow cells, inside each of which a small polyp lived: these animals, dating from the beginning of the Primary, are called graptolites because the whole creature resembles somewhat the characters of cuneiform script. Failing further information, we find in them the animal world's first attempt in the vertebrate direction. The trunk that carried the cells is called the virgula; this small chitinous axis was covered with cells arranged in rows of one, two or four tiers, inside each of which an individual lived. The virgula complete with cells therefore formed a stick bristling with geometrically arranged blisters: it is called the rhabdosome. Furthermore, recent discoveries have proved what was long surmised, that all the rhabdosomes were attached to a sort of hollow sphere, surmounted by a float, and that between the points of attachment of the rhabdosomes there were small spheres that must be regarded as reproductive organs.

In other words, we have here a colonial animal; the colony increased by the budding of additional cells from an original cell, but all the individuals remained united by their dependence on the large supporting sphere. An idea of what these graptolites must have been like is to-day provided by certain colonial Coelenterata called Siphonophora. But we no longer try, as we once did, to relate these two types of invertebrates, for new zoological relationships have recently been discovered.

Some graptolites were doubtless very similar to some aberrant animals that have existed for 75 million years and, just like the Coelacanth, have continued until to-day with scarcely any change

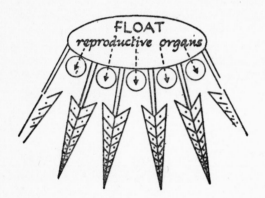

Fig. 105. Very simplified sketch of a graptolite colony; the rhabdosomes are shown pointing downward and in each of the cells is a separate individual.

of shape. They constitute an order of the Pterobranchia, and are two in number: Cephalodiscus and Rhabdopleura, which are kinds of colonial marine worms housed in small chitinous capsules and developing by budding. Now, a minute study of the structure of the cells and the method of budding shows beyond dispute that they are very similar to the graptolites. Further, it has been possible to study the larval forms of the Pterobranchia and to ascertain the outline (which, moreover, disappears in the adult) of a small dorsal nerve cord reminiscent of our own vertebral column, both by its position above the digestive tract and by its head-to-tail extent.

The epineural line continued with the appearance of the echinoderms at the very beginning of the Primary, some 550 million years ago; they probably derived from the graptolites. The earliest

types already closely resemble—at least in their general structure
—the types we know to-day, the most familiar of which are the
sea-urchins and starfish. They have a very complex network of
interconnected pockets and canals inside which the sea-water cir-
culates; the nervous system is very clearly situated above the
digestive tract and some outline of an internal skeleton makes its
appearance in the form of calcified plate deriving from the
mesoderm.

Still further invertebrates belong to the epineural line and are
definitely very like adult vertebrates, or at the very least very like
vertebrates in a larval stage. There is a long marine worm called
Balanoglossus with a small dorsal nervous axis and gill slits
through which water charged with dissolved oxygen penetrates

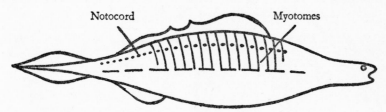

FIG. 106. *Jaymoytius*: an ancestor of the vertebrates.

to the interior of the pharyngeal cavity and makes respiration
possible.

Finally, 400 million years ago, the first undoubted vertebrate
appeared, Jaymoytius: it had the elements of a vertebral column in
the shape of a small supple trunk, called the notochord, formed of
large cells, a dorsal nervous system which, to judge by this minute
creature's large eyes, must have been already roughly differentiated
into two distinct parts which can be distinguished for convenience
as brains and marrow; further, it had a digestive tract in a ventral
position and the rudiments of fins. It was not a vertebrate properly
speaking, because it yet had no internal cartilaginous or bony
skeleton, but it already had all the characteristic elements of
vertebrate structure, that is to say, a dorsal skeletal axis corresponding to the vertebral column of more developed vertebrates,
a dorsal nervous system situated immediately below this axis (but
in the earliest vertebrates this is already enclosed in the vertebral
column), and finally a ventral digestive tract.

Ascending from diploblastic creatures to the graptolites, then following the epineural line as far as Jaymoytius; next passing to the armoured fishes, the Crossopterigii, the first amphibia, the Theromorpha, the mammals and the lemurians, man has acquired a clear picture of the living creatures which preceded him upon the earth during 1,500 million years. Man is an animal, but he has the undoubted satisfaction of assuring himself that he is an animal "unlike the others," for, says Father Teilhard de Chardin, "the animal knows, but man knows that he knows." Yet he has still to face the ultimate problem, that which is revealed as the starting point and the conclusion of this history of life and is formulated in the still unanswered question: where did life begin?

CHAPTER X

Life, the Daughter of Light

IN order to fill the gap in our paleontological knowledge that separates the appearance of life on the earth from the first already very complex living forms—the algae, worms, sponges, echino-derms, Coelenterata, etc., that peopled the Pre-Cambrian seas—we shall have to indulge in hypotheses.

But is it permissible to set ourselves this problem of the origins of life on the earth? There are some who do not think so. But whatever the philosophical conceptions each one of us may hold, we have to admit that a vast gulf exists between the creatures that form the animate world and the minerals that form the inanimate world. This gulf was one day crossed and from inorganic matter life emerged.

That is not the opinion of everyone. Eminent scientists in the last century and a few contemporary philosophers have taken a stand in favour of the eternity of life, from which perhaps even matter itself may have derived. Such seems to have been almost the opinion of Pasteur, at least at a certain moment in his scientific career, when, following his memorable experiments, he found it difficult to admit the possibility of spontaneous generation at a given moment in the history of the earth. Actually, this view (of the eternity of life) is to-day untenable. Life demands such physical conditions on the earth's surface—especially conditions of temperature and humidity—that its appearance must have come after the earth itself came into existence. Our planet, whatever its origin—which will not be discussed here—began its journey round the sun some 2,000 million years ago. Its temperature was about 7,000° C. and it was therefore nothing but a shapeless mass of free atoms revolving around one another without producing stable chemical combinations, which were impossible in those conditions. The existence of even very rudimentary living creatures is unthinkable at that epoch in the earth's history. The pyrozoa,

living creatures resistant to fire with which one physicist has sought
to people the sun, and the earth before it cooled, are only
myths.

Revolving around the sun in 365 days each of 24 hours, our
earth, which was then only a vaguely shaped gaseous sphere,
progressively cooled, and it was only when, at the end of chemical
changes with which this book is not concerned, it reached a temperature well below 300° C., that the first living forms could
survive. In our own day some bacteria, called thermophiles, live
in hot springs, but even the most hardy of them can scarcely bear
a temperature of 85° C.

There is therefore no option but to agree that matter preceded
life and that life could only have appeared on the planet at a
certain favourable moment in the chemical development of the
earth's surface. Accepting this, only two possible hypotheses remain to explain the origin of life on the earth: either life came
from elsewhere, from some other planet in the Universe (this is the
theory of panspermy), or life was born on the earth itself by
spontaneous generation as a result of certain complex chemical
reactions.

The theory of panspermy, although it was maintained by eminent scientists of the last century (Arrhenius, Lord Kelvin and
others), is not very satisfying intellectually, for to say that life was
"sown" on the earth by means of seed reaching it from an unknown
planet is to evade the problem of the origin of life and not to solve
it. Further, for the seed to have crossed interstellar space and to
land on the earth such physical conditions would have been met
(intense cooling during the journey, then heating to several thousand degrees on contact with the earth's atmosphere) that the
theory is scientifically unacceptable; no living matter could have
survived an interplanetary journey like that.

So it is on the earth itself, at a certain stage in its geochemical
history, that life was born in circumstances that must be made
explicit.

The physicist, the chemist and the biologist must explain the
transition from the inanimate to the animate. *How* was it possible
for life to be created from inorganic matter? This is a purely
scientific question requiring a scientific answer. *Why* was life
created from matter? In answer to this second question, of a
purely philosophical nature, each will explain as suits himself the

determinism of biogenesis, by reference either to transcendent or chance action; the question is beyond the purpose of this book. But in the wholly scientific field we are completely justified in seeking to know *how*—whether by chance or under the influence of some superior will—the creation of life took place, working on the basis of our existing physico-chemical and biological knowledge.

It was by "spontaneous generation," as we say to-day, that life rose out of matter. Spontaneous generation was formally condemned by Pasteur, following experiments too well known to be described here in their entirety.

It is sufficient to note that the idea of spontaneous generation is a matter of common observation to those who are content with superficial appearances. If a piece of meat is thrown away in summer, it is soon covered with maggots which may seem, if one does not look closely, to have been engendered by the meat itself. Up to the seventeenth century the idea of the spontaneous generation of mildew or small animal parasites was generally accepted in scientific circles; the literature of the period even went so far as to give very precise recipes for the most effective way of producing toads and mice cheaply and quickly. All this has now only a documentary interest. But in the seventeenth century, Francesco Redi (1626–1691) set out to demonstrate that such spontaneous generation does not occur and that the maggots were only the larvae of flies: if the meat was wrapped in paper or cloth or covered with a bell jar, the maggots would not appear. Redi's conclusions did not prove popular. It is interesting to observe that he had in fact invented the meat-safe: indeed, every important discovery made in respect of spontaneous generation (a problem that has excited scientific thought for three centuries) has led to some practical applications.

With the invention of the microscope at the end of the seventeenth century and all the new researches into microbes, the question of spontaneous generation was pursued into the realm of the invisible. The experiments went on, but people were hard to convince. In the eighteenth century, the Abbé Spallanzani, an Italian celebrated for his researches into the mechanism of generation and also for having carried out the first artificial insemination, began a resounding controversy with the English scientist Needham. During a series of experiments of rare scientific precision, he demonstrated that microscopic animalcules did not appear in culture media that were enclosed in sealed bags and had been boiled for at least three-quarters of an hour. But Spallanzani was accused of having doctored the vegetable infusions which he used in demonstrating the non-existence of spontaneous generation. Incidentally these experiments established the principles of sterilization by heat—a process which Appert, a Paris confectioner, brought into practice in 1811.

Spallanzani's researches were continued on a bigger scale by Louis Pasteur, who improved his techniques. Pasteur's experiments forced him into a lively controversy with the Englishman Bastian and with Pouchet the director of the Natural History Museum at Rouen, but the old dogma of spontaneous generation had received its death blow. From its death important practical consequences arose, particularly sterilization by autoclave and surgical asepsia.

Thus the famous adage *Omne vivum ex vivo* (everything that lives is born of a living thing) pronounced by Harvey in the seventeenth century was finally confirmed: spontaneous generation never occurs in the world to-day. For about 75 years this truth was officially accepted in scientific circles. But in 1935 the biologists were stirred by incredible news: an American named Stanley had just for the first time isolated a virus, and this virus . . . crystallized, just like a mineral!

At that time the viruses had been known for half a century. Pasteur had suspected their existence during his studies of rabies, and in 1892 Iwanowsky had produced decisive proofs. He was then studying a very contagious disease of the tobacco plant which showed up in patches of fairly regular shape on the leaves; for this reason it was called tobacco mosaic. In the full flood of Pasteurian discovery, he could not do other than search for the microbe responsible for so contagious a disease. Using techniques that are now classic, he nevertheless had to admit that he was beaten. The most effective dyes and the greatest microscopical enlargements never succeeded in making the agent of the mosaic visible; the "juice" of the diseased parts of the leaves could pass through the finest pores of the Chamberland filter, but ultra-filtration stopped nothing and the "juice" remained contagious to healthy plants. The agent of the mosaic was therefore an extremely small body, smaller than the smallest bacteria known. This body received the name "virus."

Other virus diseases were soon identified: various plant mosaics, poliomyelitis, eruptive fevers of infancy (measles, scarlatina, etc.), foot-and-mouth disease in cattle, canine distemper, cat typhus, rabbit myzomatosis, etc. But despite great efforts, the viruses of these diseases always remained invisible to the microscope and they always passed through the finest filters. Further, when an attempt was made to cultivate them in natural or synthetic media (beef, broth, egg yolk, etc.), as is done with bacteria, the cultures proved impossible unless the medium contained living cells, the normal hosts of the parasitical viruses. Until then it was thought we were faced with very primitive living creatures, ultramicroscopic kinds of bacteria which excited the interest of researchers on the theoretical level by the exasperating impossibility of isolating them and seeing them, and on the practical level by their formidable strength as disease producers, which makes them terrible enemies of man—indirect enemies, too, by the economic havoc they cause.

But when, following long and patient research, Stanley succeeded in 1935 in isolating the virus of tobacco mosaic, the problem at once took on a new aspect. Because a method had been perfected for isolating one virus, it could be hoped to isolate others and thus to study them better. This is what has happened in the last 15 years. In this, the improvement of microchemical techniques and the invention of the electron microscope have been of great assistance.

Because, on the other hand, we were faced with a living body that was able to crystallize like a mineral, a new landmark had been set up that brought the animate world closer to the inanimate. This aspect of the virus problem interests anyone who seeks the origin of life by spontaneous generation.

Now the viruses are very tiresome. For some years the question whether they are living things or not has been seriously discussed. If they are living, why do they crystallize and why do they not contain those characteristic bodies, the carbohydrates (starches and sugars) and the lipids (fat bodies) in their molecules? If they are not living, why do they reproduce themselves, ceaselessly infesting the healthy cells and making them sick?

One is also tempted to see in the viruses the intermediate beings which alone can explain perfectly the transition between the living and the non-living. But there is one weak point in this proposition: the viruses, as we know them in the modern world, are parasites that are unable to exist apart from living cells.

It is therefore necessary to study, from the viewpoint of nutrition, the relationships between living beings and the environment in which they develop. In fact there are living creatures which, like the viruses, cannot develop unless they receive the complex

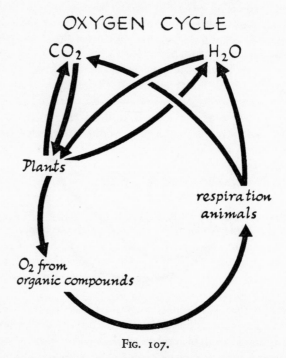

OXYGEN CYCLE

FIG. 107.

nutriment provided by other living creatures. On the other hand, other living creatures, the green plants, are capable of feeding upon inorganic substances drawn from the earth or the air. If we wish to understand the possible processes by which life made its appearance on the earth, a fairly long explanation of various nutritional methods is called for.

One can roughly say that the green parts of leaves absorb carbon dioxide and combine it with water taken up by their roots to make molecules of the simple sugar called glucose. In this process oxygen is released and passes back into the atmosphere. Part of the sugar the plants synthesize is later transformed into more or less complex nitrogenous bodies by combination with the nitrogenous mineral salts drawn from the soil through their roots. To effect this synthesis energy is required: and this energy is provided by sunlight. The plant absorbs this with the help of its chlorophyll, the green pigment present in the leaves and in some stems in the form of microscopic grains called chloroplasts. This special function of green plants has been called carbon assimilation or photosynthesis.

By extreme simplification, one can say that the net result,

NITROGEN CYCLE

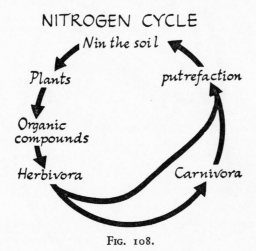

FIG. 108.

photosynthesis, is the opposite of respiration: during photosynthesis the green plant absorbs carbon dioxide and water vapour and frees oxygen; in respiration, plants, like animals, absorb oxygen and give out carbon dioxide and water vapour. Meanwhile, it must not be forgotten that green plants respire continually, while the chlorophyllian function takes place only in the presence of sunlight, that is to say during the day; respiration and photosynthesis take place simultaneously in daylight, but at night only respiration continues.

This idea of photosynthesis is very important. Because it permits the synthesis of organic compounds from mineral substances it assures the permanence of the living world. In fact, one can very roughly say that living creatures have to satisfy two essential needs. In order to live it is necessary to oxidize certain aliments and so procure the necessary elements for the functioning of the cells and therefore of the organs, that is to say, for instance, for movement, for digestion (absorption and transformation of nutri-

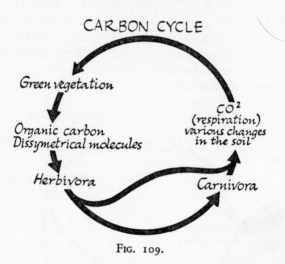

FIG. 109.

ment, excretion of wastes) and so forth. The foodstuffs that provide this energy are carbohydrates and fats. On the other hand, to live is to maintain the integrity of the organism, to replace worn-out cells; to take a single example, in the depths of the skin new cells have to be made continuously to replace the superficial cells of the epidermis, which are dead cells and are sloughed off (generally invisibly, though in certain pathological cases they do so in a spectacular fashion). This replacement of dead cells by young cells, the result of ceaseless cellular division, takes place in all the organs of the animal body except the nervous system. Certain organic compounds, including amino-acids, are necessary to the construction of living matter.

Now, animals are incapable of making these organic compounds themselves. They must find them in their foods and these are, in the end, the plants which originate these foodstuffs, directly in a herbivorous diet and indirectly in a carnivorous one. Thus there are several cycles in the living world, the only ones of particular interest being those involving nitrogen, carbon and oxygen. To describe these cycles in detail is not the business of this book, and the accompanying simplified sketches will do the job well enough.

The term *symbiosis* can therefore be applied to the association on the surface of the globe of green vegetation and animals, and their dependence on each other. By their function of photosynthesis the plants create organic substances necessary to the building up of the animal organism and the oxygen necessary for its respiration; the animals for their part give out the carbon dioxide which is necessary to photosynthesis.

When one speaks of photosynthesis, it is necessary always to make clear that only the "green plants" can carry out this process;

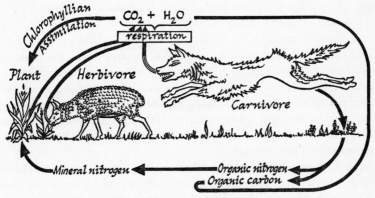

FIG. 110. The Interdependence of the Living World.

such plants are the only living things able to effect the synthesis of organic substances by using the energy of sunlight. Some other, non-green plants (certain orchids, for example) live simply as parasites on other plants, or as saprophytes on decomposing animal or plant debris (as do mushrooms). Meanwhile, it should be noted that some bacteria, instead of practising photosynthesis, practise a kind of chemico-synthesis in the soil or fresh water; that is to say they effect the synthesis of organic compounds not by using the energy derived from sunlight, but by using the energy provided by special chemical reactions (for example, the transformation of sulphuric acid into sulphur by certain sulphur bacteria).

From what has just been said, two important definitions must be given. First there are the autotrophs, living things able to maintain themselves in a purely mineral environment by means of photosynthesis or chemico-synthesis: all green vegetation and certain free bacteria (i.e. non-parasitic bacteria) are autotrophic. Then there are the heterotrophs that would be doomed to early extinction if the autotrophs should disappear: animals and mushrooms, for example, cannot manufacture some of the key organic compounds that are needed for body-building or energy production; they have to borrow these compounds, directly or indirectly, from green vegetation.

*

How, then, does the problem of the origin of life stand in the light of the two problems just discussed, of the viruses and of the carbon and oxygen cycles?

At some moment in the history of the earth these cycles had to begin; that is to say, organic matter had to arise from the mineral world during syntheses, of which the working must be made clear. Further, this organic matter had to come alive, and we must ask ourselves what is the significance of the viruses in the world today, so that we may know whether, at a certain moment in the history of life, they had been able to effect the bridge between the inanimate and the animate.

The first question concerns what was the agent of the syntheses which transformed mineral matter into organic matter. Of the very many answers that have been given, the only one worth discussing is the hypothesis formulated by Dauvillier and Desguin in 1939, known as the photochemical theory of the origin of life. The majority of biologists are now agreed that things must have happened more or less as suggested by these authors, who claim to explain not only the transition from inorganic to organic chemistry, but also, in the field of cosmic physics, to set up a plan of the evolution of the earth from its "birth" to the formation of widely differentiated living creatures.

After studying the successive chemical changes of the earth from the moment it became separated from the sun (or from a twin of the sun) Dauvillier and Desguin describe as follows the surface of our planet at the moment when life was ready to make its appearance.

Continents and oceans already existed, though it is impossible to delineate their contours. The relatively warm water of the oceans contained great quantities of carbon dioxide and ammonia, and appreciably less mineral salts than to-day. As to the primitive atmosphere, it contained only very small quantities of nitrogen and no oxygen at all; water vapour, carbon dioxide and ammonia were its major constituents. The majority of experts are to-day agreed about this lack of oxygen in the original atmosphere of the earth.

Life now made its appearance. In the first stage, syntheses of organic matter were effected from mineral elements. But these syntheses required an external contribution of energy: they were endothermic. What were the possible sources of energy at that epoch? There were four: the heat given out by the earth as it cooled, radioactivity, terrestrial electricity and sunlight. In choosing between these four sources of energy, one essential characteristic of living matter must be taken into consideration: the dissymmetry of the molecules.

This dissymmetry is extremely important. In fact, the molecules of organic compounds are not always quite alike. Though they all have the same chemical composition they do not all have the same physical structure; in any organic substance there may be two sorts of molecules, the right-handed molecules and the left-handed molecules, which resemble one another, yet are different in the same kind of way as your right hand and left hand. In other words, the molecules of organic compounds can exist in two forms, whose molecular structure differs in that one is the mirror image of the other. Physicists can distinguish between the right-handed and left-handed molecules by their action on light. It is only important for us to note this dissymmetry of the molecules in the respect that living creatures always produce right-handed molecules or left-handed molecules—that is to say always one to the exclusion of the other—while in the laboratory, when we synthesize organic compounds, we always make an equal number of both, producing a racemic mixture, as it is called. Thus although there are two kinds of glucose, living creatures always produce left-handed glucose.

Furthermore, in the matter of food, living creatures always show a very clear preference for one or the other molecular form. Thus, for example, the mould *Penicillium glaucum* that covers certain spoiled foods with a greenish fur (a related species produces penicillin) consumes only right tartaric acid, while another mould, *Aspergillus niger,* prefers left tartaric acid.

Molecular dissymmetry is thus one of the essential characteristics of living organic matter. Mineral compounds have molecules that are always all alike.

So, if we wish to explain the synthesis of organic compounds from mineral elements, it will be necessary also to explain how the synthesizing factor was able to create dissymmetrical syntheses. Now, of the four possible synthesizing agents, only light (and, moreover, a certain kind of light) was able to produce dissymmetry. It must therefore be agreed that the first organic syntheses were the work of light, were photosyntheses, just as in our day. But chlorophyll did not then exist and it is quite impossible to imagine, as some have tried to do, that it had appeared before life itself, for it is an organic substance of very complex structure, always intimately linked to living matter. But there is an important difference between the sunlight that the earth received at that early epoch and that which green vegetation uses to-day. In fact the astronomers and the geophysicists are agreed that the primitive atmosphere was devoid of oxygen and that its major constituents were carbon dioxide, ammonia and water vapour; it therefore permitted ultra-violet rays to pass through, though they are now halted by a layer of ozone, situated about 12 miles up.

In the laboratory we have just succeeded in carrying out organic syntheses by using ultra-violet rays of very short wavelengths. Dauvillier reminds us that "H. Slosse in 1898, at the Solvay Institute in Brussels, achieved the synthesis of sugars by submitting a mixture of carbon monoxide and hydrogen to the discharge of distant ultra-violet rays. D. Berthelot and H. Gaudechon in 1910 achieved the synthesis of ternary and quaternary compounds by submitting a mixture of water vapour, carbon dioxide and ammonia to the rays from a mercury arc lamp."

Syntheses of the same type are conceivable at the origin of life on earth, and one would expect them to have occurred at the surface of the oceans where there was a greater quantity of carbon dioxide and ammonia. One further condition must have been fulfilled: the organic molecules thus synthesized should be dissymmetrical. Physicists, of whom Pierre Curie was the first, have demonstrated that only one physical agent is able to effect such a synthesis: circularly polarized solar light.

It is impossible to give a definition of this light in a few lines, for reference would have to be made to ideas in physics that have no place here. It is sufficient to say that light can exist in two forms, natural or polarized. Further, light can be polarized either in straight lines or circularly. When light falls on the surface of the water, some of the rays (those which touch the water at an incidence under 37 degrees) are plane-polarized. If these rays thereafter happen to pass through a doubly-refractive crystal (quartz, for example) circularly polarized light is produced.

Can we conceive that sunlight was circularly polarized at a certain moment in the history of the earth? The answer is: yes. It was simply necessary that this light should pass through a quartz crystal. It may certainly be admitted—and this seems to me to be the best hypothesis—that quite by chance the light that achieved the first photosyntheses had been circularly polarized, and we may see in this the fundamental cause of dissymmetry in living matter.

Others refuse to admit such a chance, and seek to attribute the dissymmetry to some cosmic phenomenon (such as the direction of the earth's rotation, the direction of terrestrial magnetism, etc.). This opinion has some value but no scientific fact has so far come to its support.

THE DAUVILLIER AND DESGUIN THEORY

1. Synthesis of organic matter from carbon dioxide gas and ammonia under the influence of circularly polarized sunlight.

*

2. Appearance of reproduction centres (virus stage).

*

3. Appearance of membranes around centres of reproduction (bacteria stage).

*

4. Appearance of pigment (cyanophyceae stage).

*

5. Definitive differentiation of the nucleus and the cytoplasm (protozoa stage).

Thus, the light of the sun, rich in short-wave ultra-violet rays that had not been halted by the primitive atmosphere (that was devoid of oxygen and therefore of ozone) effected a photosynthesis of carbon dioxide, ammonia and water-vapour, and caused the appearance of vast layers of gelatinous organic matter which may be compared, for convenience, to the white of egg. These gelatinous masses were presumably denser than water, and when they formed on the shores of the warm seas they must have settled at the bottom of the briny lagoons. Moreover, it was on the sea shores that solar light had the greatest chance of encountering the crystals which changed it into circularly polarized light.

This is perhaps the place to recount briefly the picturesque story of Haeckel's monera, the subject of one of the most resounding quarrels that have ever taken place regarding the origin of life.

Haeckel is not unknown to the reader, since it was because of his ideas—partly mistaken, however—about the origin of man that Dubois left for Java and there discovered his *Pithecanthropus*. Fully and imaginatively exploiting evolutionary ideas, then much in vogue, Haeckel conceived between 1870 and 1890 a vast panoramic picture of the origin and development of life on the earth. Haeckel wrote the first history of life, but because of the considerable gaps in our paleontological knowledge at that date, his history was a little imaginative. Further, Haeckel did not hesitate to invent the intermediate types necessary to complete his general outline and thereby created the man-ape which was actually discovered in due course. At the origin of life the German naturalist placed the moneron, a sort of organic gelatinous particle of completely rudimentary structure. In 1878 one of Darwin's most ardent supporters, Thomas Huxley, discovered at the bottom of the ocean, during deep oceanic dredges, a sort of amorphous organic jelly corresponding in every way to Haeckel's moneron. Huxley dedicated his discovery to the German scientist by naming it *Bathybius haeckelii* (*Bathybius* signifying "a creature living in the depths"). But a year later he had to retract hurriedly and to confess that *Bathybius*, of whom so much had been expected, was only a gelatinous precipitate of calcium sulphate that had absorbed some organic matter in its descent.

But to return to the organic matter that had settled in large viscous sheets at the bottom of the lagoons that fringed the oceans of the infant earth: a step forward was certainly made when

Dauvillier and Desguin succeeded in explaining the synthesis of organic matter from mineral elements.

Meanwhile, this mass of organic matter has to be studied from two viewpoints: the new physico-chemical conditions that its creation had established on the earth's surface, and the fact that living organisms had not yet made their appearance. The transformation of this inert organic matter into living organic matter has yet to be explained.

From the chemical point of view, organic matter tends to react with the oxygen that its synthesis has freed. This reaction takes place in our day through the phenomenon of respiration, the oxidation of organic matter which regenerates carbon dioxide and water vapour. Another transformation process occurs in the modern world: during fermentations promoted by certain bacteria, organic matter is progressively destroyed until carbon dioxide and water vapour are liberated once again. Although respiration and fermentation may be two very different phenomena, they achieve the same result and provide living creatures with the energy necessary to the manifestations of life; in other words they animate the living world.

What then was to happen, since, in the absence of living creatures, this organic matter was still in metastable equilibrium? Dauvillier and Desguin's reply is that, since these organic compounds were in existence and they had to be dissociated into carbon dioxide and water vapour, not only was life on the point of appearing (all the necessary physical and chemical conditions being in conjunction) but the appearance of life was an absolute necessity, for organic matter could not remain in this state of metastable equilibrium. Thus, to follow Dauvillier and Desguin, the organic syntheses effected by ultra-violet rays became the cause of life, the appearance of which was inescapable from the moment these syntheses began. This is certainly one of the most interesting aspects of the photochemical theory of biogenesis.

We have still, however, to make the transition from inanimate organic matter to living matter. In this connection we must recall the studies carried out on viruses. In the end these viruses are only specially complex molecules: each virus is a molecule. Although it does not possess the power to breathe, that is to say to oxidize organic matter into carbon dioxide and water vapour, the virus is able to reproduce by repeated binary fission; one virus particle

divides into two particles, each of which proceeds to divide into
two, and so on. So, in order to explain the evolution of these
sheets of organic matter, Dauvillier and Desguin justifiably suggest the formation in the midst of this matter of molecules of
great size, some of the largest of which at a certain moment acquired the power to multiply by binary fission. Stanley, who
studied the tobacco mosaic virus, made several pertinent remarks
in this connection. By assimilating the usable foods in their environment, the virus molecules reach such a size that rupture
into two daughter-molecules becomes inevitable; further, this
rupture is favoured by the fact that similar electrical charges
accumulate in the molecule and naturally repel one another, thus
leading to fission.

In this way Dauvillier and Desguin conceive the appearance in
the midst of this newly formed organic matter of "centres of
chemical activity endowed with the ability to reproduce themselves, or at least with the capacity for binary fission." These
centres therefore present one of the principal characteristics of
life: the ability to reproduce. These centres "feed" themselves by
breaking down organic matter through fermentation.

*

The development of these centres of reproduction into more
complex living forms is relatively easy to explain. The surface
phenomenon associated with large molecules have been studied
by physicists and provide the basis of an explanation of how
membranes could appear in the midst of this organic matter,
partitioning it off without depriving it of its continuity, a process
comparable to what we can see happening in colonies of bacteria.
Respiration and fermentation, assuring the energy necessary to
the fulfilment of vital phenomena, brought about a continuously
increasing liberation of oxygen; in its turn, this oxygen was partly
transformed into ozone, a gas which soon formed a protective layer
that prevented the ultra-violet rays of the sun from destroying the
first living creatures.

Finally, complex pigments like chlorophyll were able to make
their appearance and the first photosyntheses began. The essential
cycles characteristic of life on the surface of our planet were
established. The Cyanophyceae and the Protista were not long in
appearing.

To explain even in a hypothetical fashion life's first stages on the surface of the earth is therefore, in the end, to reply to three questions. Here are the questions and the replies that Dauvillier and Desguin give.

How were complex organic molecules able to develop from relatively simple mineral substances? Dauvillier and Desguin answer that the ultra-violet rays given out by the sun (rays of short wave-length), passing through an atmosphere devoid of oxygen, effected the combination of carbon dioxide and water vapour to form formaldehyde, simultaneously liberating oxygen; this formaldehyde afterwards polymerized into simple sugars. The chemical reactions are formulated thus:

$$CO_2 + H_2O \rightarrow HCHO + O_2$$
$$6HCHO \rightarrow C_6H_{12}O_6$$

After the fashion of green vegetation to-day, combinations took place between these sugars and certain nitrogen compounds, effecting the synthesis of the proteids for which the formula is as follows:

$$C_6H_{12}O_6 + NH_3 \rightarrow amino\ acids.$$

How was the agent of this synthesis able to create dissymmetrical molecules? Dauvillier and Desguin's reply that short-wave ultra-violet rays, passing accidentally through a doubly refracting crystal, had alone been able to create dissymmetrical molecules.

How was the power of reproduction acquired within this organic matter? Dauvillier and Desguin say that the great size of certain molecules bearing similar electrical charges and therefore capable of repelling each other resulted in reproduction by binary fission. Organic matter in a form resembling a modern virus was evolving.

Finally, two particularly original points in Dauvillier and Desguin's theory should be emphasized; firstly, in the succession of geochemical changes, the formation of the layers of organic matter was inevitable at a certain moment in this evolution; secondly, the formation of this organic matter was the cause of life, the appearance of which was also inevitable at a certain moment in the history of the earth.

A certain number of scientists have taken a stand in advance against this photochemical theory of the genesis of life, by de-

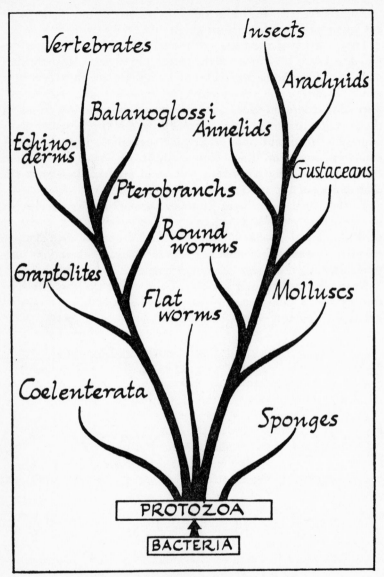

Genealogical Tree of the Living World

claring that it is impossible to put forward any reasonable hypothesis whatever to explain the origin of life.

They assert that the theory of probability makes it necessary to visualize a very long time for the creation of highly dissymmetrical molecules, like all the molecules of living matter; they believe it would require much longer than the 1,000 million years at our disposal. Leconte du Noüy declares that it is impossible to admit the existence of life in the first ages of the earth; it is all the more impossible to formulate an acceptable scientific hypothesis to explain the genesis of life at any moment whatever of terrestrial evolution, since this hypothesis will be in contradiction with the probabilities of the appearance of dissymmetrical molecules.

To these objections Pierre Auger has provided a pertinent reply by remarking that in a molecule of great size certain atoms in small number alone play a vital role. And the appearance of these essential atomic combinations, by pure chance, is not very improbable.

So the light of the sun has played and still plays a key role on the surface of our planet. It has created life and, by means of chlorophyll photosynthesis, plays its part in maintaining it.

EPILOGUE

SO the History of Life comes to an end.

And, as usual, a short conclusion is required. But writing a conclusion should be something better for the author than carrying out a traditional procedure, and something better for the reader than passing a distracted eye over three or four pages so as to be able to say with a clear conscience that he has got to the end of the book. In a work of this kind at least, a real conclusion should be, first, a clear and precise summary of the preceding chapters, and next, an expression of the sentiments that have moved the author in his task.

To summarize the history of life is a very simple thing. For convenience, this book has been intentionally written in reverse, because it seemed preferable to place a discovery in its historic framework rather than to display the results drily, being in this way more or less easily understandable. Was it not the case of the Piltdown fraud, or the miraculous catch of the Coelacanth, that in recent years has drawn the attention of men to the problem of our biological origins? Moreover since there was no question here of presenting a treatise for experts, the diversification of the ammonites into numerous genera and species, or the fundamentals of the classification of armoured fish at the beginning of the Primary, would have been of small importance. Thus both the shape and the numerous gaps in this book can be justified.

To summarize the book is first of all to present in their chronological sequence the various living forms which have followed one another on the surface of our globe for at least 2,000 million years. It is, in other words, to recapitulate the nine essential dates in the history of life, and to express in the form of a genealogical tree the lessons of this chronology. The tree is derived largely from the works of two great contemporary French zoologists, Lucien Cuénot and Albert Vandel, whose philosophical ideas I shall shortly elucidate at greater length.

Here are the dates in approximate figures—approximate because the present uncertainty of geological measurements scarcely allows us to reckon them more exactly, and also because I have deliberately rounded some of them off to make them clearer and easier to remember.

From 3,000 to 2,000 million years ago the earth was detached from the sun or from its twin.

1,500 million years ago life made its appearance on the earth and successively passed through the "virus," "bacteria," "cyanophyceae" and "protozoa" stages.

1,000 million years ago the protozoa ruled over the seas and, beside them and deriving from them, the simplest forms of organization in the invertebrate world.

500 million years ago the principal types of organization of the animal kingdom were already fixed in their main lines, numbering about 30. One of these types, the vertebrates, seemed privileged.

400 million years ago certain vertebrates began to adapt themselves to life in the air: hence the appearance of fish with lobed fins and lungs.

350 million years ago life set out to the assault of the dry land with the most primitive amphibians.

200 to 100 million years ago the reptiles achieved the first conquest of the continents; that is to say, life for the first time definitely freed itself from its servitude to an aquatic habitat.

100 to 1 million years ago the mammals achieved the second (and penultimate) conquest of the continents, which they carried further than the reptiles. They possessed in fact a system of thermal regulation, a method of reproduction and a nervous system better adapted than those of the reptiles to the conditions imposed by life in the air.

500,000 years ago man, in the form of pre-man, made his appearance on the surface of the earth and distinguished himself especially by thought and language.

*

This outline, expressing our essential knowledge of paleontological matters, should lead first of all to this conclusion: evolution is an indisputable fact, and this fact is moreover now well supported by a mass of proofs which, besides pathology, derive from such varied branches of knowledge as anatomy, physiology, embryology, geology and geography.

Evolution, once again, demonstrates that on the surface of the earth the simplest living forms were progressively transformed into more complex forms; these theories are to-day accepted by all biologists and philosophers worthy of the name, despite some attempts at refutation made with evident awkwardness by certain persons who may be either mere publicity-seekers or ignorant fanatics.

During the second half of the nineteenth century, the anti-transformists sometimes enjoyed themselves by bringing forward proofs which more recent discoveries have broken down. Further, the misinterpretation of the writings of transformists clashed violently with some religious minds which often had no desire to admit that man had descended from the ape—which Darwin himself never said.

This long misunderstanding has now ended and there is no case for dwelling long upon it here. What need is there to work over the facts of current observation and experiment in order to make them agree with religious convictions which do not require it? On the contrary, the Abbé de Lapparent, one of the greatest of contemporary geologists, said one day: "If I had to summarize in a few lines the main events in the history of the earth, I would copy out again the first paragraphs of Genesis"—where in fact can be seen the successive appearance of light, the continents, plants, fish, terrestrial animals, and finally man.

The fact is that evolution is an incontestable fact and that we must now try to elucidate its principal laws, workings and philosophy.

*

Probably no one has been able to elucidate so precisely a panoramic view of the world in evolution than has Father Teilhard de Chardin in a paper called "La vision du passé" delivered in 1949; for it is not only animal life on the earth's surface that changes and during the ages presents an ever-renewed face, but, indeed, the whole universe, the living and the non-living. Assimilating the teachings of biology and the recent work of geologists and astrophysicists, Father Teilhard shows that in the last 10 years we have succeeded in perfecting a veritable "means of condensing time." This machine, of a very special type since its existence is purely intellectual, is the creation of very diverse scientific techniques, the result of progress in mathematics, physics, chemistry, biology and paleontology, a progress which goes from statistical methodology to paleontological micro-examination, by way of optics, electronics, radioactivity, and so on.

What does this "means of condensing time" teach us when we try to co-ordinate its results into a coherent whole? It teaches us that despite the abrupt variations that have affected this or that part, animate or inanimate, of the earth during some millions or thousands of millions of years, the universe in evolution is the centre of slow and continuous movements, one of the most important of which is orthogenesis. By this word we mean that systems in evolution, despite the failures they show, despite the blind alleys in which they sometimes become involved, seem always to direct themselves towards a well-defined end, which is eventually reached despite all obstacles. And not the least of these orthogeneses—probably the most important—is the one revealed by the progressive complication of the nervous system. From the simplest bacteria and protozoa to complex mammalian forms, by way of Coelenterata, Echinoderms and lower vertebrates, the living world in evolution reveals a progressive tendency to the superior organization of the nervous system, with perfect co-ordination of movements and rapid response to external stimuli. It is in this sense that Father Teilhard can speak of "the irreversible complexification and cephalization of the nervous systems."

Viewed in its details, there is something disconcerting about the history of the universe, for it seems that one cannot deduce any comprehensive law. If one seeks, for example, to draw up a genealogical tree for the human species, one can do so only with difficulty: from the pre-apes of the early Tertiary to *Homo sapiens* of the Quaternary one can only trace a dotted line. If one tries to set up a genealogical tree for any family in the animal or vegetable kingdoms, the result is just as disappointing, even when there are —as in the case of the horse—many intermediate forms and this abundance of missing links seems to permit, at first sight, the tracing of an uninterrupted line. Never, in practice, is it possible to decide with certainty that one species directly derives from some other.

The problem is further complicated by the fact that usually

various attempts have been made in the direction of any given animal type, although all but one of these attempts were doomed to failure. What can be called the rhinoceros type came into being five or six times in the Tertiary without surviving, not to mention identical forms produced by some reptiles of the Secondary. Therefore there is, says Pierre Teilhard, a "fan-like" evolution; only one line in this fan-like process is able to rise above the others and continue its evolutionary destiny.

Finally, if we take our attention away from the general aspect of a line to its beginning, we discover that other law that Father Teilhard calls "the law of the concealment of origins," a fairly characteristic example of which is given by the history of the Coelacanth, or more exactly by that of its cousins, the Rhipidistia, from which all the terrestrial vertebrates of aerial respiration have derived: all the Rhipidistia have vanished long since and nothing but a very few fossil specimens are known, and they certainly seem to have lived only a few hundred thousand years. Similarly, we do not know how, or by what intermediaries, the transition was made between reptiles and mammals, between pre-apes and men, and so on.

Father Teilhard asks: "How is it that, although everything is born, in a Universe in genesis, we can find nothing of a real beginning?" The answer is that the forms which were at the origin of a zoological group were necessarily not very numerous, were very plastic and therefore very fragile. In conclusion the author cites this example: "In the case of undoubted beginnings, of which we have direct evidence (automobiles, airplanes, etc.), is it not certain that, if our engines were fossilized, future paleontologists would never (except by unearthing a museum) suspect or recover the rudimentary types which preceded the most perfected, most standardized and therefore most abundantly distributed machines."

So, justifying the extrapolations to which the paleontologist who claims to trace a history of life on the earth must devote himself, one can only conclude with Pierre Teilhard, "that it is therefore from the observation not of the past but of the present that the study of the processes of origins emerges."

Regarding the processes themselves, enough has been said in the foregoing pages about the clash between neo-Darwinians and neo-Lamarckians, but over and above these quarrels of the biologists it is more interesting to conclude with an outline of the

main lines of a philosophy of evolution, first following Albert
Vandel and then, once more, Father Teilhard de Chardin.

*

For Vandel, a panoramic view of the history of life leads to the
conclusion that man seems to be not only the consummation of
evolution but, even more, that all evolution seems to have developed in relation to man, that is to say that it has had as its
aim the appearance on the earth of an individual with a large brain,
with an intelligence much more developed than that of the most
intelligent of the animals. And this individual is man. Two typical
sentences from the work of Vandel summarize this point of view
well: "Man is the epitome of the world" and "Man rests on the
immense edifice of the organic world which maintains and explains him." Thus the universe in evolution has at last become
aware of its evolution, an evolution that is itself an "emergence of
the consciousness beyond material and organic things."

This leads us quite naturally to an outline of the principal
conclusions which Father Teilhard de Chardin has reached in an
essay—now already some years old—called *Du préhuman à
l'ultrahumain*.

By analogy with the existence of the atmosphere and its extension, the stratosphere, the German geologist Suess at the end of
the last century named the terrestrial crust the lithosphere. Thus a
succession of superimposed beds takes shape and the whole constitutes our planet, the Earth. Between the lithosphere and the
atmosphere is sandwiched the biosphere, that is to say the sphere
of living creatures, animals and plants which, by their very presence, considerably modify the superficial aspect of the earth's
crust. Above this biosphere Father Teilhard suggests inserting a
new sphere, the "noosphere" or the sphere of thought, having
been struck by the ceaselessly growing importance of the human
mind during the past few thousands of years.

Now this "noosphere," he adds, stretches to-day over the whole
surface of the planet, which it envelopes completely. It is a recent
phenomenon.

At the beginning, 25,000 years ago for example, only a few
"centres of thought" existed, scattered about the globe where the
first *Homo sapiens* was to be found (Cro-Magnon, Chancelade,
Grimaldi), while the two Americas were yet unvisited by man.

Gradually, these scattered "centres of thought" spread from their points of greatest concentration, spread out and reassembled in proportion as the human masses stretched into the area and reassembled: "On a thinly inhabited planet," Father Teilhard writes, "the various civilizations succeeded in growing and keeping together without serious trouble." But in less than a century, as a result of industrial development, a compression of the human masses has developed so that to-day they are not only in contact but they interpenetrate both economically and intellectually.

The human substance has "planetized" itself, says Teilhard, and from this "planetization" will come an ultrahuman phenomenon that we can only foreshadow and which will have its centre in the "noosphere."

Probably some of us immediately think of the superman. It must be said at once that the biologists, despite a certain mastery of the mechanism of transmitting single hereditary characteristics, are still very far from creating supermen; between producing giant wheat on the one hand and superman on the other there is a wide gap.

On the other hand, the extension of the "noosphere" to the entire planet and, whether we like it or not, the phenomena of collectivization (in the wider sense and not in the political sense) which result from it, could well lead us towards a sort of psychical superman without visible anatomical modifications.

This is certainly a debatable idea, but we cannot remain unaffected by it. We are here on shifting ground where I would not want to lead the reader except to show to what ideas biology and paleontology are leading us to-day.

The story of paleontology ends neither well nor badly. Because each of us writes a few words or a few lines of it each day, the greater part of the time without knowing it, it is a story without end.

INDEX